HEROES OF GOD SERIES

This is a book in the HEROES OF GOD series.

Other books in the series include:

PAUL, THE WORLD'S FIRST MISSIONARY
by Albert N. Williams

JEREMIAH, PROPHET OF DISASTER
by Virginia Greene Millikin

QUEEN ESTHER, STAR IN JUDEA'S CROWN
by Laura Long

SIMON PETER, FISHER OF MEN
by Albert N. Williams

DAVID, WARRIOR OF GOD
by Juanita Nuttall Jones

JOHN THE BAPTIST, PROPHET OF CHRIST
by Slater Brown

MARCUS AND NARCISSA WHITMAN, MARTYRS
ON THE OREGON TRAIL
by Ann West Williams

JOSEPH, SLAVE AND PRINCE
by Laura Long

The series will include books about Luke, Elijah, John the Apostle, Martin Luther, Francis of Assisi, John Mark, and other biblical, historical, and modern church pioneers of our religious heritage.

The HEROES OF GOD series is under the general editorship of Albert N. Williams and Ann West Williams.

WILLIAM TYNDALE
MARTYR FOR THE BIBLE

WILLIAM TYNDALE, MARTYR
From Holland, Herwologia Anglica, 1620

HEROES OF GOD SERIES

William Tyndale

MARTYR
FOR THE BIBLE

by

CATEAU DE LEEUW

ASSOCIATION PRESS

NEW YORK

WILLIAM TYNDALE, MARTYR FOR THE BIBLE

Copyright, 1955, by Cateau De Leeuw

FIRST PRINTING

Library of Congress catalog card number: 55-7419

 55

Printed in the United States of America
American Book–Stratford Press, Inc., New York

CONTENTS

1. OUT INTO THE WORLD
(1522)

MASTER WILLIAM TYNDALE sat in a circle of his friends. His gaze wandered over the smoke-blackened interior of the White Horse Tavern, as if he were trying to fix it in his memory.

For more than a year the tavern had been known in the town of Cambridge as "Germany" because so many of those who frequented it came together in order to discuss the new writings of Martin Luther. They were students and masters, priests and friars. Some of them owned Luther's books, which were being smuggled into England, and these were read and argued over by the little band with unwearying enthusiasm.

On Tyndale's left sat young John Frith, handsome and talented, who occupied a favored place in Tyndale's heart. On his right was Thomas Bilney—"Little Bilney," as he was affectionately called. Beyond him, at the head of the table, sat Robert Barnes, an Augustinian friar. A kindly man, and a witty one, he was also,

Tyndale thought, a little vain and given to loud speaking. He was between Frith and George Constantine, whose smooth face was now creased in patent sorrow.

It was late, and many of those who came regularly to meet with them had gone to their rooms for the night, for they had to be up early the next day. But those who remained did so to honor their friend who was leaving them on the morrow.

"How we shall miss you!" Frith said suddenly. He lowered his voice a little, for even in this place it was not wise to speak too loudly of certain things. "No one else can make the Scripture so clear or so inspiring to our eager ears."

"He is well versed in it," Barnes commented. He turned full toward Tyndale. "Even when you were at Oxford, you read the Scripture privately to certain students and fellows of Magdalen College, teaching them to seek for truth and knowledge therein."

Tyndale nodded sadly. "What a strange world is this, that even in the universities no man is permitted to look upon the Scripture until he has been nourished upon the false principles of heathen learning for some eight or nine years. By that time he may have built such a wall within his own mind and heart that he is full shut out of the understanding of the Scripture."

Frith cried, "And he must swear that he will hold no opinion condemned by the church. But *what* such opinions are, he is not supposed to know!"

Little Bilney's voice was soothing. "Think how much

farther we have come than our fathers! The New Learning has done much to set men's minds free." And then
he added, as an afterthought, "Although, of course,
they are not supposed to think their *own* thoughts!"

It was true. The New Learning, which had come to
Italy so many years before with the rediscovery of the
old Greek and Latin classics, had found a home even
in France and Germany within a few years, but it had
been late in coming to England. The natural result of
this intellectual renaissance—and the new freedom for
men's minds—had been the Protestant movement
among churchmen.

Thinking back on his early youth, Tyndale remembered what an eager student he had been, particularly
of languages and logic, and how he had been sent to
Oxford while still a young lad. There his first gropings
toward knowledge and creative thought of his own had
been stimulated. Even then, he recalled, he had been
drawn to the study of Greek by the reputation of the
great Dutch scholar Erasmus, who had earlier taught at
Cambridge. Tyndale had soon determined that only
through the study of Greek would he be able to inter-
pret accurately the message that had been left to mankind in the New Testament.

The Bible had been translated many hundreds of
years ago from the original Greek, Hebrew, and Ara-
maic into the formal tongue of the church, which was
Latin. This Latin version of the Bible was known as the
Vulgate. Only the priests and a few highly educated

laymen could read it at all, and there were many priests whose education was so poor or whose mental capacity was so limited that they could only sound the words without any understanding of the meaning behind them.

Ever since the New Learning had appeared upon the intellectual horizon of Europe, scholars of Greek had realized that the Vulgate, although a fine piece of work for its time, contained errors that their new studies in the ancient languages revealed, and Erasmus produced not only the Greek Testament but a new Latin translation of it.

But Tyndale and his friends felt that it was still not enough to correct the Latin version of the Bible, for the great mass of the people had no knowledge of Latin, and even to those who could read their native tongue, the Bible was a closed book.

"If only the Scriptures were printed in English!" He did not realize for a moment that he had spoken aloud. But the eager way in which his friends leaned toward him, the sudden burst of their voices, speaking together, told him how well they agreed with his wish.

"The church will never permit it! If all men could read the New Testament, for example, they would have their own interpretation and that would surely be frowned upon."

"Yes, this way the populace must accept whatever is offered. This way there can be no quarrel with the church's rules and penalties, bans and penances. None dares dispute because none has the knowledge to argue."

"Some of us have, but it would be madness to do it."

"Martin Luther broke the way. Not only did he translate the Bible into German, but he made so simple a translation that even the poorly educated could read and understand."

"But look at the ferment it has brought about! Small wonder that the church forbids it!"

"It has brought about great good, too. For the first time, men in Europe are reading the words of Christ for themselves. There is a religious awakening greater than any that has been seen before."

"Some would not call it that. Some would call it revolution and anarchy."

"Why, think how many people have the Scriptures now in their own language. Germans, Italians, Spanish, French, Bohemians, Dutch—"

"But not the English," someone said, and a sudden silence fell.

The words echoed in Tyndale's ears. For a long time something had been stirring in the back of his brain—a dissatisfaction and an ambition, inextricably mingled. The dissatisfaction was expressed by all that his friends had been saying. And more, much more. But the ambition was one which he had scarcely acknowledged even to himself before this time.

It was behind his reasons for leaving Cambridge. Tomorrow he would depart from Trinity Hall, ending the student life of years to become chaplain to Sir John Walsh and tutor of his children, in Little Sodbury, Gloucestershire.

It would be good to be in his home county again, but he felt a pang at leaving a life so congenial to one of his tastes. Despite the hardships, he had loved it. The narrow rooms, so barely furnished, so cold and drafty in winter, so poorly tended, were all he had known for many years. A hard pallet for sleeping, the simple, spare diet of the hall, the unheated lecture rooms, the dirty floors, were an old story to him. But so, too, were the delights of learning, the heady joy of argument, the deep satisfaction of teaching.

Yet he felt he must go forth into the world and meet mankind in its daily life, must leave the cloistered atmosphere of study for the brisk air of reality.

Frith seemed to have been following his thoughts. There was an unusual closeness between them, although they had known each other for only a short while. He said now, "You come from near there, don't you?"

Tyndale nodded. "I spent my childhood in Slymbridge, and my brother Edward is seneschal receiver of the lordship of Berkeley in that area."

"Little Sodbury is near Bristol, is it not?" Again Frith seemed to have been thinking with him.

"I shall be able to observe life in the city as well as in the village, no doubt."

"Perhaps you will even preach there?"

"Perhaps."

His mind, so intent on envisioning the future, had already left Cambridge behind, and when his friends walked back to Trinity Hall with him, he was able to leave the familiar gathering place of the White Horse Tavern without a backward glance.

2. THE AIM AND THE TARGET

(1522)

THE TWO LITTLE SONS of Sir John Walsh were in the hands of their nurse, and Tyndale went to the great hall for dinner with an easy mind. His stay here at Little Sodbury had been happier than he had anticipated. Already he was looking forward to the coming meal, for Sir John had told him last night that there would be special guests this morning.

There were always guests at the huge table of Sir John's hospitable manor house, and now he saw that some of them were clustered before the fireplace. A stout traveler was holding forth. He was wrapped in a furred cloak beneath which might be glimpsed his startlingly "blistered" breeches—slashed in the German fashion. His feet, in broad-toed shoes, were planted far apart, and he spoke with authority.

"I would have you know," he was saying as Tyndale approached, "that there is much disquiet in London. Our good Queen Catherine having had no child since the Princess Mary five years ago, men are saying in the streets and the alehouses—yes, and in the council chambers, too—that our dear island may yet become the plaything of some foreign power should the princess be married."

Someone said, "There is talk of betrothing her to Spain, when she is already betrothed to the Dauphin of France, and that is bad enough! Now, should we have Spain over us—"

There was a murmur of distress from the throng of listeners. "Some would have the king make Henry Fitzroy, his natural son, the heir to the throne, and they say he is thinking on it, but if that should fail, what will England do?"

Tyndale knew they were remembering the unhappy days before the Tudors, when Lancaster strove with York for control of the country, and civil war ravaged the land. He said, "Now, what would be so terrible if we should have a queen over us? Is not a woman endowed with God's spirit, as well as a man?"

They wheeled toward him, incredulity written large upon their faces. "A woman? To rule us?" they echoed. "It would be madness!"

A visiting priest pushed his way toward Tyndale. "What foolishness is this?" he protested. "All men know that women are lesser beings, and not fit to rule. To hear you talk, one would think you would have them fit to preach, too!"

Tyndale hesitated a moment, and then he spoke

boldly, "It is true that women are not fitted to rule or to preach, for both are forbidden them. Yet, should there be a necessity for either, might they not, through God's help, do everything as well as men?"

With one accord the others shouted him down. Tyndale would have answered all of them had there been time, but a commotion at the door stopped their mouths. A great rushing to and fro of servants, the neighing of horses and shouts of riders, took their attention.

Sir John Walsh, tall and handsome, strode to the door to welcome the newcomers, his lady Anne beside him. A princely figure paused just inside the doorway and surveyed the gathering with cold eyes.

"Bid you welcome, my lord abbot," said Sir John, bending low, while his lady kissed the old man in greeting, as was the custom in those days. "We are happy to have you in our humble house."

The old man's progress into the hall was slow and stately. Everyone hurried forward to see him, to bow before him, or to kiss his hand. Tyndale, arriving after most of the others, was met with a sharp look.

"Ha! Are you the priest I have been hearing about?"

Tyndale looked puzzled. Sir John said smoothly, "Master Tyndale is tutor to my sons. He preaches sometimes in the little church of St. Adeline behind us here."

"And elsewhere, too, I have heard," the old abbot snapped. "In too many village churches, and on St. Austin's Green at Bristol, where the rabble will always gather to hear some firebrand spout nonsense. It has come to my ears that there is a Lutherish taint to some of your chaplain's sermons."

Sir John glanced at Tyndale, as if bidding him speak for himself, and Tyndale said simply, "There is nothing in what I say to disturb anyone. I only preach God's law."

"But not the pope's," the abbot cried angrily, "and it is better to be without God's law than the pope's. See that you mend your ways."

Tyndale was silent, biding his time. But after the board had been laid, and the visitors had been well fed with teal and chicken, with boar's head and beef, he led the abbot gently into discussion.

Much mellower, now that his uncomfortable journey of the morning was past, and well warmed by the lavish hospitality of the Walshes, the abbot unbent enough to put forth an argument or two. Then Tyndale began to quote more and more from the Scriptures, and the old man stumbled into a morass of words from which he could not extricate himself.

When he would retort, his knowledge was so faulty and his Latin so poor that Tyndale was almost moved to pity him, yet he did not. It was bad enough, he thought angrily, that ignorant priests should know little Latin, but this was an abbot, a "learned" man, a man of power in the church.

At last his disgust overcame his natural reserve, and he cried emphatically, "If God spare my life, before many years I will cause a boy who drives the plough to know more of the Scripture than do you!" The table fell into shocked silence.

That afternoon, when Tyndale went to walk in the woods near the manor house, he thought of the numbers of visitors he had defeated in argument at the Walshes' table these past months. Some were the ignorant, clumsy clergy of the neighborhood; some, like today's abbot, were men of weight in the church. With all of them he had launched into eager discussion, for this was what he had been used to in Cambridge, and before that, in Oxford.

But these men had no desire to sharpen their wits or to increase their knowledge. They had no interest in their church positions other than the income they derived from them. They might be versed in the study of tithes and mortuaries, but of the Scriptures they knew little and cared less.

What had distinguished the talk today was the fact that for the first time he had said publicly what had lain buried in his heart for so long. He repeated his own words, nodding a little. "A boy who drives the plough." Here was an ideal to which a man might well dedicate his life.

Tyndale was not surprised when, some time later, the abbot and other high clergy invited Sir John and his wife to a banquet. The moment they returned home, he knew what had happened, for it was written in their faces, half embarrassed, half determined.

They repeated to him all that they had been told at the banquet, and Tyndale realized that his discomfited enemies had been at some pains to think up a few arguments that would hold weight with his patron. But when he started to answer, Lady Anne spoke quickly.

"Look you, Master Tyndale," she said, "there was present there a certain doctor who may spend two hundred pounds a year, another, one hundred pounds, and another, three hundred. What do you think? Is it reasonable that we should believe you rather than such great, learned, and wealthy men?"

Tyndale knew that there was no answer he could make at this time. His patrons' pride in having such a fine Cambridge scholar as tutor for their sons had been lost in their mortification at what must have been said to them by the wealthy and great of the church.

And so he set about making a translation of one of Erasmus' works, which he put into English because there were many things, especially in the preface, that he wanted his patrons to read; Erasmus' name was so great that he knew it would have weight with them where his own words would not.

When he put this translation into Sir John's hands, he realized that the happiness of his future here depended upon it, and he was not long kept in suspense, for Sir John was enthusiastic about it and insisted on reading certain passages aloud to Tyndale, forgetting, in his excitement, that it was Tyndale himself who had made the translation.

Not long after Tyndale had won back the support of the Walshes, all the priests of the neighborhood were called to appear at a sitting of the Chancellor of the district.

Tyndale went to the meeting with an inner feeling of unease. He did not know why the meeting had been called, but he was well aware of the dislike in which he was held by the local clergy, and he feared there might be some unpleasantness in store for him.

When his name was called, he stood up. In the thinly veiled glances of anger and contempt with which the other priests regarded him, he read condemnation. The Chancellor, John Bell, snarled at him, "You, William Tyndale—*Master* William Tyndale—you are here to answer this list of accusations." His finger rapped the paper he held in his other hand.

Now that Tyndale knew what was before him, he was calm. He realized that one false step at this time might well be fatal for his future, and he held his feelings in stern check.

"What are the charges?" he asked. "And who has made them?"

Bell did not deign to answer this last. He began to read from the document. Tyndale was a heretic in sophistry . . . a heretic in logic . . . a heretic in his divinity . . . and so on and on. The list was ridiculously long and there was no ground on which any of the charges could firmly rest. Tyndale knew that. But he also knew that these men were determined to see him humbled, or at best removed from his present post of influence.

With outward calm but inward fury, he proceeded to refute the charges, one by one. He made a point of justifying everything he had said by a quotation from the New Testament, and if he had been of a mind to be amused, he could have been well entertained by watching the faces around him as they struggled to follow his smooth and fluent Latin.

And at the close of every refutation he asked again, "Who made this charge?"

Every priest of the district was there that day, and he knew that his accusers must be among them, but not one would own to the position of accuser, nor would the Chancellor tell him who had made the accusations.

Indeed, these persistent inquiries seemed to bring Bell's temper to the boiling point, so that at last he leaned toward Tyndale and spewed forth a mass of invective.

"Child of iniquity!" he thundered. "Would you, with your heretical depravity, lure the simple minds of the people into the pestilent, scandalous ways of thought of the Lutherans? Are you so blinded by wickedness that you would defile the flocks of the Lord, and, with your vicious erroneous words, lead them into the profanities of your belief? Vile stirrer of the stinking pools of heresy, what have you to say? Why should such carrion as you not be removed from this district altogether?"

The early sixteenth century was a time of unbridled language, and now Tyndale was raged at in a manner he would never forget. But when Bell asked him this question, he stood a little straighter and said with quiet emphasis, "I am content to go wherever you wish, in any part of the country, if you will give me ten pounds a year to live on, and bind me to nothing but to teach and to preach."

In the end, perhaps, it was the knowledge of Tyndale's powerful patronage in the great Walsh and Poyntz families (Lady Anne Walsh was a Poyntz) that made the Chancellor moderate his attitude. Tyndale was finally allowed to depart, "neither branded as a heretic, nor trammelled by any oath of abjuration."

But he saw all too clearly that Gloucestershire was not the place for him, after all. This final display of clerical arrogance convinced him that religion, as it was administered by the church, was not sufficient for the spiritual nourishment of man. The great truths were still there, but buried so deeply beneath layers of meaningless laws and rituals, distorted by so many delinquencies and bigotries, that most men could no longer find them.

There was one sure way by which men could be led back to the great teachings of Christ, and that was through a knowledge of those teachings as they were contained in the Scriptures. If these were available to men, in their own language . . .

He felt in his heart that this was the answer, but he knew he could not accomplish what he desired by staying in the comfortable manor house of Sir John Walsh. To be allowed to translate the New Testament he would need to have the backing of someone powerful in the church, for no man might do this on his own authority, and also he should be where the printing could be done if he succeeded in his ambition.

London was the answer, of course. And who could be a better choice for patron than the new bishop of London—erudite, scholarly, powerful Cuthbert Tonstall?

Yes, London was the place for him.

3. LONDON INTERLUDE

(1523–1524)

THE STREETS WERE SO CROWDED that Tyndale could scarcely push his way through the human barrier, and at one corner he was forced to halt so long that he mounted the steps of the house near which he was standing so that he could see ahead to discern the cause of the delay.

A sea of heads jostled beneath him and in the distance, where a cross street brought a little daylight to the scene, he could make out a procession of men, some afoot and some on horseback, all finely dressed in orange-tawny coats. He spoke to the man beside him, who was also craning his neck to see the parade in the distance.

"Is it the king?"

The man laughed scornfully. "It is the man who sets such a costly court our king cannot match it," he replied. "That is the livery of our cardinal, Wolsey."

"Wolsey?" Tyndale echoed. The parade of liveried

men had been succeeded by a fine litter, and the litter by more mounted men. "But he . . ." He stopped. He could not say to this man—a modest tradesman by his dress—what he thought. This worldly show was ridiculous for a churchman. Yet he should not be surprised; he had seen the splendor of Wolsey's triumphal visit to Cambridge three years before.

The tradesman spoke again. "Some say he is seven times greater than the pope himself. But it is hard to see how that can be. Tom Wolsey was humbly born like myself. Now, how could such as I hope to be that great?"

Tyndale's lips compressed into a thin line, and he bit back the bitter words that formed upon his tongue. There would be no use saying them now. Better to save them and write them at some later date, for surely a display like this merited the attention of thinking men and, if he could have his way, he was the man to bring such things to their attention.

Oh, there had been others, he knew, who had dared to preach against the fashionable living of clerics and priests. But this was the head of the church in England. This was Wolsey, whose example should be an inspiration to all beneath him. Tyndale turned away from the tradesman. The procession was past, and people were moving in the streets again.

He set his mind to happier contemplation. Sir John had given him a letter to Sir Harry Guildford, controller of the royal household, a man high in King

Henry's favor. Surely his recommendation should provide an interview with Bishop Tonstall.

He put all thought of the discomfort of the trip behind him. There had been muddy roads, crowded at times with travelers, at other times blocked by herds of livestock or geese moving slowly toward the market places of the great city. The inns had been dirty, their beds and floor rushes full of fleas, though the food had been good and the post horses adequate.

But he could not help remembering certain things he had heard and seen on the journey: the dissatisfied talk among farmers; their grumbling at the herds of deer that ruined their corn during this Fence Month of midsummer; their muttered rebellion against the heavy tithes and church fines; the empty churches in many villages, with no priest to serve them; the great enclosures for sheep pastures that had once been fertile farmland; the gibbets with dangling corpses of vagabonds, homeless men for whom there was no longer work on the land and who had been executed, so stringent were the laws against begging.

He could dismiss none of these things, and they came back to him with renewed force when he thought of the pompous display he had just witnessed.

With little money in his purse, he lived simply, waiting for his chance to be interviewed by Tonstall, but he did not mind this. He was grateful to his family for the support they had given him during his long years of study, and he had saved his stipend from the

Walshes. If he were taken under Tonstall's wing, the problem of money would no longer be a burden to him, and he could devote his whole time to the work ahead. He had labored long over his letter to the bishop, and he had taken it himself to the episcopal residence. Now he could only wait.

When the money in his purse was almost gone and there was still no call from the bishop, Tyndale began to cast about for some sort of employment, and it was then that he met Poyntz, a man from Gloucestershire and a distant relative of Lady Anne Walsh, who arranged that he should be allowed to preach in Poyntz's parish, St. Dunstan's in the West.

Tyndale wrote his sermons with care. He always strove to do everything as perfectly as possible; he always labored to improve himself so that he might do better in the future. And it was so with his brief service in St. Dunstan's in the West.

Because of this, and because he was so earnest in the things he preached, he made a great impression upon Humphrey Monmouth, a wealthy cloth merchant with a great house in the city, a member of that powerful trading corporation, the Merchant Adventurers. Monmouth was a man who had traveled as far afield as Jerusalem—an extraordinary journey for those days—and he was accustomed to patronizing men of letters with unfailing liberality. This was the man who heard Tyndale preach one Sunday, and who was greatly taken with the young priest.

There came a day when the summons from the
bishop arrived, and Tyndale, eager and hopeful, went
to the palace. All the things he had heard of Cuthbert
Tonstall passed through his mind as he threaded the
crowded streets: that he was still young, accomplished,
learned.

Tyndale carried with him a translation that he had
made from the Greek of the orator Isocrates, as proof
of his scholarship, and he rehearsed in his mind again
and again the arguments he would present.

But Tonstall, nervously striding up and down the
small antechamber, scarcely glanced at the carefully
copied translation. He tossed it upon a table, and
crossed the room to stare out of the window.

"I have four chaplains now," he said, his back to
Tyndale, as if he did not want the see the other's face
while he made his pronouncement. "What need have I
of a fifth? My house is full. You had best seek employment elsewhere. I have nothing for you here."

He could scarcely have made it plainer. Tyndale
opened his mouth in protest. "But I have a special reason for wanting to be attached to your household," he
said. It was not easy for Tyndale to be humble before
such an autocratic manner. "I have it in mind to make
a translation—"

"There are too many translations now," Tonstall interrupted, not waiting to hear what it was that Tyndale wished to translate, although he must have learned
it from Sir Harry Guildford, "and not enough learned

men to read them. I am sorry. You will have to seek elsewhere."

He resumed his nervous pacing, beckoned to a secretary who lingered just outside the door. Tyndale moved away. He would not plead further. This was not the man he had expected at all. He had thought the friend of Erasmus would be kinder to one whose scholarly aims were so closely related to the church.

Without the support of a powerful churchman his intended translation of the New Testament was an impossibility, for it was against the law to translate it, much less print it, and he would need the backing and acknowledgment of at least a bishop, who would work for its acceptance by other highly placed churchmen.

He went out into the open air and breathed deeply, trying to make the leaden weight in his chest lighter by the act.

What now? Was he to end his days in ignominy—he who had had such great plans for the future? He walked down the street, his lean ascetic figure braced against this crushing disappointment.

Humphrey Monmouth proved his savior. No sooner did he hear of Tyndale's rejection by the bishop than he offered the homeless priest a place in his own home and enough money to serve his needs.

"Ten pounds a year, my good friend," he said, putting one great beefy hand upon Tyndale's thin shoulder, "to pray for my mother and father. Surely the prayers of one like you will be well received in heaven. And there is a room for you beneath my roof, and a place for you at my table. You are a learned man, and I shall be proud to have you as my guest."

Tyndale soon settled down to life in the cloth merchant's house. It was a busy place, with agents forever coming and going, with news from the Continent brought firsthand by men who spent their lives traveling to and from their snug little island on matters of business. The cloth business was thriving; more and more of England's farms had been "enclosed," or turned into sheep pastures, for wool was the prime commodity. And no wool could surpass the English wool.

Flemish weavers had long had the bulk of the market for finished cloth but now the English, too, were making cloth, and their markets for it were constantly expanding. There was talk of monies and exchanges, of ships and the sea, of politics and religion, at Monmouth's board, and Tyndale heard it all. He no longer offered quick argument as he had at Sir John Walsh's manor house; life was teaching him to be more cautious, was teaching him that there was much he could still learn, and here he was learning it.

He went out seldom, being deep in the study of the New Testament and making his first efforts at a translation of it. But when he did venture forth, he constantly saw things that sickened him. London was the home of the rich and powerful; it was also the home of the poor and wretched. To watch Wolsey's stately progress each day from York House to Westminster, to see the cardinal dressed in crimson silks and satins, sables, wearing embroidered gloves and shoes inlaid with pearls and diamonds, was to underscore the contrast between his splendor and the filth and rags of the poor.

Tyndale heard many stories about him and about the bishop of London at Monmouth's table. "They say Wolsey's very cook wears a velvet jerkin and a chain of gold about his neck!" . . . "What mockery is this, that a servant should wear velvet to spatter grease upon it?" . . . "And gold chains to dangle in the soup kettle, no doubt!" . . . "They say he has eight hundred people in his retinue." . . . "That is true enough; I think I've seen them all myself, at one time or another!"

And of Tonstall: "He makes a fine show, but he's still in debt for having been made the bishop of London." . . . "Some say he's been offered the see of Ely; now, that's even wealthier than London." . . . "Yes, but he's refused it, for it would mean he would have to borrow even more."

Tyndale spoke. "Why must we be spiritually governed by men who buy their places in the church? Why must we make obeisance to a pope who holds these offices for sale?"

"Hush, man," his neighbor said, digging a friendly elbow into his ribs. "Not so loud! Even in a house like this, that smacks too much of heresy."

Tyndale doubted if he had been heard by any but those immediately around him, and they were men of whose loyalty he felt sure. Many businessmen had a scarcely concealed enmity for the church, which stemmed from the days when the church had frowned on all profit but its own. This enmity was now focused upon the person of Wolsey. He felt there was little danger to him in what he had said. But Monmouth had heard, and Monmouth sought him out later to speak to him.

"How goes your work, Sir William?" he asked. In England, it was customary in those days to address a priest as "Sir." His kindly eyes questioned more than his tongue.

"Slowly," Tyndale confessed. "I find it difficult at times to concentrate, for there is much noise and disturbance."

"I thought as much," Humphrey Monmouth said. "You have been with me now for more than six months, and you have heard much of what goes on here. So you must know that I have friends in the Merchant Adventurers who are as anxious to see the Scriptures printed in English as I am. As you are."

"I have gathered as much."

"Then you probably know, also, that some of these men have been instrumental in the smuggling of Luther's works into this country. It is not easy, but a merchant who deals constantly with other merchants on the Continent finds it easier to do these things than other men."

He looked long at Tyndale, then said slowly, "Some of us feel that it might be easier for you—safer, too—

to complete your work in some snug place abroad. Then, when you have finished and the Testament is printed, it shall be our work to see that it is brought here and distributed."

Tyndale smiled bitterly. "There was no place for me and my work in the palace of the bishop of London; now it would seem that there is no place for me in the whole of England."

Monmouth said hastily, "We are thinking of you, Sir William, when we urge this. For you know as well as we that no English version of the Scripture has been authorized, and that whatever comes forth now will be suspect and dangerous to handle."

"I know it," Tyndale acknowledged.

"There will be no need to worry about money," Monmouth assured him. "Find a place where you can work and a printer to print what you have written, and we shall see to the money as well as to the distribution."

For a moment Tyndale felt as if he were being swept away from all that he knew and loved by a tide of circumstance that he could not combat. And then his resolution came to the fore, and the instinctive courage that was to be his staff for the rest of his life made him lift his head proudly. "I can be ready at any time," he said quietly. "What country were you thinking of? Germany?"

4. TREACHERY IN COLOGNE

(1524–1525)

THROUGH HIS ACQUAINTANCE with a German merchant at the Steelyard, Humphrey Monmouth had arranged for Tyndale to stay with the Widow von Emersen while he was in Hamburg, and her comfortable home was opened to him. Even better for one who could not speak German—although Tyndale was well versed in many languages—her nephew went with him to Wittenberg when he left the busy port.

Matthias von Emersen was young. There were not many years between them, but Tyndale often felt himself old enough to be the father of the youth. They traveled together congenially enough, ascending the Elbe River to the university town of Wittenberg where Matthias was going to study.

To Tyndale, Wittenberg was much more. Outwardly, he knew, it was a small town of only two thousand inhabitants, the seat of a rather new university. But it had one distinction that no other city of Christendom could boast: it was where Martin Luther lived.

To a man like Tyndale, forward looking and sincere, it was a city of great promise. Were not the very bases of the future being hammered out upon the anvil of great minds in this place? Where could he better study Luther's translation of the Bible? What finer scholars could he take counsel with than those he would find at Wittenberg? There would be a library there, and the books he would need for his work.

Matthias said, above the heavy clop-clop of their horses' hooves, "We're nearly there, Sir William, and soon you can say whatever you think with no fear of unsympathetic hearers. It's not like Hamburg, where the pope's party is riding in the saddle, and where you have to lock the doors before you come out with what might sound heretical to other ears. In Wittenberg, Frederick the Wise gives us real protection."

His horse skirted a small pile of manure where two ragged children of a German peasant were playing, and Tyndale gazed back at them. The farmer's hut was in better condition than most, and the holding was the most prosperous he had seen. He spoke of it, adding, "I had thought our common folk in England had little enough, but the peasants in Germany have almost nothing."

Matthias nodded. "You may not have heard it, not being fluent in our language as yet," he said, "but there have been disquieting reports of late. There are uprisings in southwestern Germany and near the Swiss border. They say the people have risen under some

new leader and are demanding what they call 'justice.'
They will not succeed. They have tried before to better
their lot—more than twenty years ago they tried it and
were defeated—and no doubt this time the end will see
them worse off than before they started."

He did not sound too concerned, and Tyndale
frowned a little. He had found the contrast between
the wealth of London's nobles and prelates and the
harsh poverty of the city's slums bad enough. Yet he
had already seen enough in Germany to know that
there was even greater contrast between the hopeless
lot of the peasants and the careless richness of their
overlords. In England, at least the men who tilled the
soil did not live under such shameful circumstances, although the growth of the wool industry had brought
hardship to many of them.

He said, "Surely men were not made to live in such
filth and misery as this?" His gesture swept from horizon to horizon. "Surely the beasts of the field have better food and shelter than these poor souls?"

Matthias shrugged uneasily. "Perhaps. But give them
an inch and they'll take a league. Freedom to them
means only the right to pillage, to burn, to spill blood."

Tyndale said nothing, but he was disturbed by the
callousness of this attitude. Always aware of the hardships of the poor, he could not enjoy his own bread
for thinking of their hunger. Perhaps, if all men could
know the Word of God, could know of his love for

them, they would no longer crush one another so heartlessly.

When they got to Wittenberg, they first found lodgings for themselves, and then Tyndale went to the university to register. Matthias did not do so at once; he had made some new friends—young men of spirit and exuberance like himself—and he felt that there was plenty of time in the future for study.

But Tyndale could hardly wait to get started on his great work. He went to register on May twenty-seventh. At the last moment some remnant of advice given him by Monmouth came to mind and he used the name Guillelmus Daltin, in case there was someone in town who might report on his activities to England.

"Why Daltin?" Matthias asked. He had seen the name on his own signing three days later.

Tyndale smiled, the shy, rather mischievous smile that illumined his face rarely. "There are two syllables to my name," he said. "Does it matter which one comes first?"

"Dal-tin, Tyn-dale," Matthias repeated, with a chuckle. "That is clever."

Soon Tyndale felt ready to begin his translation. He had a New Testament of Luther's, given to him by one of the German merchants of the Steelyard in London; he had all the books of the university library at hand, grammars and dictionaries, and, above all, an immense will to work. With the Latin Vulgate, Erasmus' Greek text as well as Erasmus' Latin translation and notes, and with Luther's German translation before him, he went steadily ahead. Translating, comparing, studying, his days rounded quickly into a steady routine.

He could speak German well now, and he could always talk with fellow students in Latin, the universal language of the scholar, if he felt his German inadequate. It was in meeting other people, in studying the changing scene of Germany's Reformation, that the modern language was to be a help to him.

This was a time of turmoil in all Europe, and Tyndale had not been long in Wittenberg before he realized how little England had been affected by it until now. Her very insularity had protected her from the waves of violence and discontent that were everywhere sweeping over the people.

For more than sixty years past, the Holy See had annexed a greater and greater temporal power. Its interference was constantly felt in politics, accompanied by an untold amount of intrigue. This had led, in turn, to an overextension which made such demands upon the papal treasury that soon the very positions within the church were for sale to the highest bidder.

These things were bad enough. To be ruled spiritually by a group of men who thought more of their purses than of their souls tended to drive good men away from the tutelage of the church, forcing them to find religious sustenance within themselves or from other sources. What had brought the Reformation to a head, however, was the moral disintegration that finally led to the sale of indulgences, of dispensations for marriages that would otherwise have been forbidden, and even of absolution for sins, whether already committed or only anticipated!

Men are so constructed that they cannot lead really happy lives with an uneasy conscience. Few men, indeed, even in those turbulent times, were able to persuade themselves of their innocence when it had been purchased with gold from a pardon-seller. Those who had a naturally strong moral fiber were repelled by such tactics. Their repugnance did not focus only on the man who offered pardons for sale, but on the religious body behind the man that not only permitted but encouraged such sale.

There were many fine men within the church, men who deeply regretted this turn of events and who hoped that reform could come from their own members. They were the clean core who brought it through these years, scarred but living. There were others whose souls were so repelled by all that they had seen and heard and read that they could see no hope for salvation except in a clean start. These were the men who gave the Reformation its strength. And they knew where to find the basis they would need. It lay, as it had always lain, in the Bible. Here, they felt, was the Word of God, pure and undistorted. Here was the foundation for a true Christianity.

As Tyndale worked, deep in the labor that he loved, he often reflected how great a need there was for the

Bible in England. He had seen the need for it growing in the past ten years.

He smiled to himself. He would make as fine a translation for his countrymen as Luther had made for his. He would put the immortal words into language that even the poorest Englishman could understand and profit by. The words sang through his brain as he wrote, words of beauty and strength, words of comfort and exhortation, words of fire and spirit.

The months passed quickly. When Tyndale awoke from his trance of work, he discovered that it was spring again. Another year, and another great stride along his life's pathway. The translation was finished, and now it was time to have it copied and printed. His money was low, and he remembered that Humphrey Monmouth had promised to send him another ten pounds when needed. Even more, he now needed the money that certain English merchants had pledged for the printing of the New Testament.

He went back to Hamburg to send for the money and to wait for its arrival, then returned to Wittenberg, where he was joined by William Roye, a friar who had been sent to him by Monmouth to serve as his secretary.

For six weeks the two men checked and rechecked; Friar Roye copied while Tyndale made his last corrections. It was a time of stern devotion to the task, and it was with surprise that Tyndale, hurrying toward his lodgings one June day, heard the bells pealing for a wedding and spied a wedding party on the steps of the church porch. He was startled to see that the bridegroom was Martin Luther, who was this day taking Katherine von Bora for his bride.

Thoughtfully, Tyndale went on his way, reviewing in his mind the many changes he had seen in the past year. In Germany, the marriages of priests and nuns were everyday affairs; church images had been destroyed; the forms of worship had been altered. These things had become commonplaces to the Germans, but to Tyndale they were new and strange, for in England there had been no change. He felt, on the whole, that the air had been cleared in many ways, that religion could once more breathe and live, and become the comfort and inspiration of mankind.

On the debit side of the ledger, however, was the Peasants' War. The disturbances which had begun the year before in southwest Germany had spread like a fiery epidemic until huge areas were engulfed in it. The peasants had good reason for their rebellion—few of Europe's lower classes were as repressed and mistreated as the German peasants. Milked of every resource by the princes and the church, they suffered a miserable existence, scratching a bare minimum from the earth for their own sustenance, wretchedly housed and clothed.

Tyndale's sympathies had been with them when they first began their revolt. Even when word of their atrocities reached Wittenberg, even when they got bestially drunk, when they pillaged, burned, and murdered, he could find excuses for them in the life from which they had sprung.

But their leaders had been unable to control them. Soon the destruction became a mad orgy of blood and loot. Luther, in horror at what had received its initial impetus from his words, had proclaimed sternly that what he had advocated was religious freedom, and religious freedom only. He wrote a tract in which he attacked the peasants and gave his support to the established forces of law and order. His words would have doomed the revolt to failure even if the common folk had not been so poorly led, so easily duped, so selfishly intent on aggrandizement.

Group by group the peasant bands were trapped and exterminated, or scattered into harmless units. The princes did not dare kill too many of them—after all, there was the land to be tilled, and they needed the peasants for that as well as for the taxes they could pay. There were still many who could return to their hovels, disillusioned, poorer and hungrier than they had been before, discouraged and depressed. They were completely cowed.

Tyndale sighed to himself as he remembered this tragic waste of human life. Men had yet to learn to live kindly with one another. The Word of God must be set in their hearts.

Tyndale set about choosing a place to have his work printed. Wittenberg had printers, but was too far inland. Cologne was on the river Rhine, with its heavy commercial traffic. It would be much easier to ship the completed sheets to England from that city, for the English Merchant Adventurers had agents there. Moreover, Cologne was near Frankfort, where the great book fairs were held spring and autumn.

This decision reached, Tyndale and Friar Roye traveled overland to the Rhine, where they took ship for Cologne.

"We shall have to be careful," Tyndale warned his assistant as they sat in the bow of the barge. "Cologne is a papist city." He felt the warning was necessary, for Friar Roye, he had found, was given to bragging and indiscreet gossip.

Roye stared at him. "This Peter Quentel, the printer you have chosen," he said drily, "is a papist himself. Will we not be putting our heads into the lion's mouth when we deal with him?"

But Tyndale was confident. "He is to print three of Luther's little books, I have heard on good authority. Surely their content would be as dangerous for him to print as this will be." He tapped the bulky parcel of manuscript that had not left his possession for a moment.

As if to clinch the matter, he added, "Business is business to any printer, and Quentel is like the rest of them. If he cannot read English, so much the better for him. He will make no effort to know what he is printing as long as he is paid well for his work."

Tyndale was right. He and Friar Roye soon settled into a routine that demanded their constant presence at the printing shop, for the German printers could not understand the language they were setting into type. Any errors they made had to be spotted at once and corrected before it was too late.

Although there had been a popular uprising in June in Cologne, it had lasted only two weeks, and by this time the prince-archbishop was in complete control again. This made the city a dangerous place for Tyndale, and he and Roye were compelled to remain in hiding during their stay.

One day Tyndale came from the small back room where he had been going over some newly printed sheets, to hear Roye talking boastfully to one of the printers in German. "There is something here that will startle the world," he was saying. "You Germans have had the chance to read the Scripture in your own language for some time now, but my countrymen have had nothing in their own tongue. They'll have good cause to remember me and my work," Roye cried, puffing out his chest with pride. "We'll have all England turned Lutheran before—"

Tyndale's touch upon his arm silenced him. The printer, who had been standing by with nodding head and foolish smile, turned quickly back to his work. Tyndale cried angrily, "Can you not hold your tongue, man? Must you clack to every fool who would listen?"

Roye's flushed face darkened. "He is too dull a dolt to know what I was talking of," he defended himself. "And besides, he is a Lutheran man himself."

Tyndale was not appeased. "And do you think only dolts can do this work?" His hand swept around the busy printing shop. "And do you think *he* will keep silent when you could not?"

Roye was silenced and sullen for several days thereafter, and Tyndale, who had begun to sleep lightly for fear that Roye's words had traveled to unfriendly ears, relaxed a little. He noticed that the printer to whom Roye had been speaking avoided his gaze whenever he entered the shop, as did several of his fellows, but he was too busy to ponder over it.

Each time that he or Roye wished to come into the front of the shop they had to make sure that the coast was clear, and several times they were herded into the back room by Quentel himself when a certain short, pompous little man came to do business. Tyndale asked Roye who the man was, and the friar said, "John Dobneck, he that is known as Cochlaeus. He was dean of St. Mary's Church in Frankfort, but when the people rose this past April, they put him out of the town."

"What does he here?" Tyndale demanded. "I have heard he is an archenemy of Luther." He could feel fear rising within him. Not for himself, but for his precious work.

"He is overseeing the printing of a manuscript," answered Roye unconcernedly.

Still nothing happened, and the days went on as before. The printing of Matthew was finished, and the printing of Mark well advanced. Tyndale and Roye, keeping to their small room one evening, were startled by a pounding on the door.

They stared at one another for a blank moment. Who knew of their lodging save Quentel and the agents of the Merchant Adventurers here in Cologne? Tyndale was the first to recover. Opening the door a crack, he said, "Who is there?"

The man who answered was breathless from running, and they lost his name. He cried, in a hoarse whisper, "You must go—quickly! Dobneck has informed on you to the city officials. They are coming tomorrow to seize what has been printed. And you—"

Tyndale interrupted fiercely. "How did he know? Who told him?"

There was a sudden silence, broken only by the man's heavy breathing. Then he said humbly, "Someone—several of us—knew what you were having printed. And Dobneck had us to his room for wine."

"And someone talked," Tyndale finished bitterly. "When was this?"

"Several nights past," the man confessed. "But we have only just learned—"

Tyndale did not listen to the rest. Several nights past! Who knew how much had been accomplished against them in this time? Was there still a chance?

He whirled on Roye. It was Roye whose loose tongue was behind this catastrophe. "Get horses! Now! To-night! A pack-horse, too. As soon as it is light, we leave."

He turned back to the printer, rewarded the man with a coin. And when they had both gone, he himself hurried to Quentel's house. He and the printer un-locked the silent shop, bound the stacked, printed sheets into bundles, carried them back to Tyndale's lodging.

At dawn, Tyndale and Roye, together with the pack-horse carrying the manuscript and the printed sheets, left Cologne as secretly as they could, and fled up the Rhine to Worms.

5. SUCCESS AND PERSECUTION
(1526–1527),

THE CITY of Worms, to Tyndale's thinking, had two great advantages. It had recently gone over to the Lutheran cause and would be safe against further tongue-wagging by the incorrigible Roye; and it was the home of one of the finest printers in Germany—Peter Schoeffer, who was, moreover, friendlier than Quentel had been.

In record time—from late September to February—a printing of six thousand copies was finished.

Printing, in those days, was a slow process, although it was incredibly faster and more productive than the old way of copying a book by hand upon parchment. Every piece of type had to be set by hand, the slow-drying inks were applied by leather buffs to the forms, and the damp paper was printed on one side at a time by a hand-operated press. Then the printed sheets were set aside to dry and stacked carefully.

Books were usually sold in sheets, which the buyer

had bound to suit himself. This method was not only the common one in practice at the time, but it was also an advantageous one from Tyndale's point of view, for the flat, folded sheets would be easier to transport and conceal than bulkier bound books would be.

Now, with the New Testament in printed form at last, Tyndale supervised the shipment of some of the books to the great spring book fair at Frankfort, which was patronized by buyers from all of Europe. Others were sent overland to Antwerp for shipment into England by some of the English merchants there. It was too hazardous to send them at this time down the Rhine where they would have to pass Cologne, and where the authorities were doubtless on the lookout for just such contraband.

His first great labor over, Tyndale was able to turn to these matters. And it was with distinct relief that he realized one problem could be solved. All the time that Friar Roye had been with him, he had been compelled to suffer from the other man's impetuosity, from his wagging, persuasive tongue. Now, at last, he could part with him, for he was no longer needed.

Roye was not perturbed at being dismissed. "You'll not need me any more?" he said lightly when Tyndale told him of his decision. "It's just as well. It's time for me to move on anyhow. I'm no dull merchant to pack books in bales and cart them from pillar to post!"

"Nor am I," Tyndale retorted. "But it does small good to translate the New Testament, to see it printed, and then turn about and forget it. There was only one reason for the labor in the first place—that men might learn the Word of God for themselves. They cannot do that if I let the sheets lie in a warehouse."

Friar Roye shrugged. "That's your affair," he said. "I'll take my pay now, and go. I have something new in mind."

Tyndale looked at him sharply. "Here in Worms?"

"Never fear," Roye laughed. "I'll not bother you and your holy ways. I'm for Strassburg."

Tyndale sighed. It was a relief to know that Roye would no longer be about to plague him with his wildness. Yet he felt, too, a certain responsibility for the Englishman, for there was no denying that Roye was a fine scholar and had given him invaluable help. He said, taking out his purse, "Here is your due. I am sorry there is not more, but you have borrowed in advance. This is all there is."

"No matter." Roye turned at the doorway, a crooked smile on his lips. "I'll find someone to pay my way. Why work for money when you can talk it out of your fellow man?"

Tyndale turned away from the door when he had gone. Well, he thought, now I am alone and I can start the work I have long thought about. He sat down at his table and picked up a Hebrew grammar.

Even in Wittenberg, while he was engrossed in the task of translating the New Testament from the Greek, he had begun the study of Hebrew to fit himself for the translation of the Old Testament. Now, he felt, he could make his first attempt.

And soon he might have lost himself comfortably in the joys of scholarship and interpretation, had not word come almost at once from England concerning the reception of his translation of the New Testament.

First of all came news of the difficulties into which one of his Cambridge friends had fallen. Robert Barnes had been haled before Wolsey and had, after questioning, agreed to recant on what he had said in a sermon. He and four merchants of the Steelyard were forced to cast faggots upon a great public burning of Lutheran books at St. Paul's Cross.

When he read this, Tyndale shook his head, for the foreign merchants of the Steelyard were really much safer from interference than the citizens of London themselves. From the time of Edward III, the Hanseatic merchants had spent privileged lives within this great fortified enclosure of their warehouses and homes. The Steelyard was almost like a little country within a country, with its own laws, its own walls.

Reports came to Tyndale steadily now, from friends in England and from those members of the Merchant Adventurers who were supporting him in his work. Great merchant guilds maintained their own courier systems, with regularly scheduled trips, so that he was kept well informed of the news from home and was able, too, to send word back to his friends, provided he did so cautiously.

He learned that copies of the New Testament, which had been quietly circulated among those who were interested in religious reform, had begun to appear in such numbers that Cardinal Wolsey was worried. There had been several episcopal conclaves held to decide how best to prevent their distribution. Cuthbert Tonstall, bishop of London, warned the London booksellers against handling them, but there was a good profit to be turned in the sale of these forbidden books, and it was doubtful if many of them obeyed him.

By the end of October there was another burning of books at St. Paul's Cross. This time the books were Tyndale's translation of the New Testament, and Tonstall himself preached the sermon against them.

Much of the fury that his translation aroused among the churchmen came from Tyndale's use of certain words. The Greek word *ecclesia* he had correctly translated many times as "congregation" instead of "church"; if the hot arguments which ensued seem strange today, it is because sixteenth-century England had known only one church—the Roman Catholic Church—and Tyndale was trying to bring out the idea that all men are members of God's congregation. The Latin word *caritas* became "love" in his New Testament instead of "charity," again a truer, broader interpretation.

But, worst of all in the eyes of his clerical enemies, Tyndale had used the word "repentance" instead of "penance," emphasizing the need for personal conscience and a contrite heart rather than certain acts prescribed by the church.

Throughout his translation, Tyndale remembered his vow concerning "a boy who drives the plough" and used simple language which any Englishman who could read would be able to understand. But, though his language was simple, it was extraordinarily vigorous and powerful, and it was enriched by a variety and clarity that only a man of immense vocabulary could have employed.

Tyndale was a true artist with words, for he made a point of choosing them with great care, realizing how easily misunderstanding can arise, and misinterpretation as well, unless each word is exact in its meaning and in its place in the text. It is this which has made his language so timeless, for his translation was so apt that men have carried many words down through the ages—words that might otherwise have been lost to the language—simply because he had placed them so well in the book which so many were to read and study. In his work, English finally emerged as a tongue worthy of the greatest thoughts, the most poetic phrases.

This poetic quality, the wonderful rhythm that seemed to be completely natural to him, made his translation continue to live and sing over the centuries. Previous to him, whatever translations had been made of the New Testament into English were either completely literal or awkward and stiff, and, being in manuscript only, were not available to the people. But it was not only because he was a poet, but because he felt the message so keenly, that Tyndale's work had such flow and majesty.

As Tyndale read the troubling letters from home, he saw that he had been right to leave his country. Even though there were times when he knew a deep longing for the lovely English countryside, even though there were times when his ears strained for the sound of English speech, he realized that he could never have accomplished his work if he had remained.

Soon the demand for the New Testaments was so great that an Antwerp printer, Christopher van Endhoven, made copies of the Worms edition, and these books began to come into England in such numbers that the English ambassador to the Low Countries asked to have van Endhoven arrested.

But such measures did not stop the production of the books. There were other printers to take it up, and the copies printed in Worms and sold through the Frankfort book fairs continued to appear. The English prelates were furious. To Tyndale's amusement, he learned that one great clergyman had been reduced to trying to *buy* up all the copies that he could, in order to take them off the market!

And then, one day, came word of a much more serious nature, and he understood that the arrest of Robert Barnes had been only the beginning.

Tyndale was in Marburg, visiting his friend, the scholar Buschius. The landgrave, Philip of Hesse, had recently founded a university there, and Buschius was one of the professors. The two men sat talking before the fireplace in the German's comfortable quarters.

"It is good to be here," Tyndale said, stretching out his legs to receive the warmth. "Worms is well enough, but Marburg is better, for your prince is one who has truly embraced religious reform."

Buschius nodded. "We are fortunate," he admitted, "although there are many places in my country where you and I would both be in danger of our lives. Here we are safe." He looked into the fire a moment, then added, "Not so long ago we thought of your country, England, as a haven where peace still reigned, even though it was still under the thumb of the pope. But now . . ."

"Now?" Tyndale inquired, lifting his head with a quick movement, for he had sensed something behind the other's words.

Buschius was surprised. "Have you not heard? But no, perhaps not. You have been to Frankfort, and then on the road here. There was no chance for you to receive letters from your friends. *If* they had dared send them!"

At this, Tyndale sat upright. "Now, what is this?" he demanded. "Has there been trouble?"

"In this century there is always trouble," Buschius declared. He sighed heavily. "You knew a Thomas Bilney when you were at Cambridge?"

"Little Bilney?" Tyndale cried. "Why, of course, I knew him well. What has happened to him?"

"He has been arrested in Norwich where he was

spreading the gospel, and brought to trial in London, we hear. My friend in the Steelyard, who wrote me of this, says he was a great influence for good, and had converted many scholars to the Lutheran beliefs."

"Little Bilney!" Tyndale echoed again. He sprang to his feet, as if physical action would help to ease the shock. "But he is so gentle—why would they—"

"It is beginning, my friend," Buschius said sadly, "in your country, as well as in Europe—the persecution of those whose faith differs in the slightest from the dogma of the Roman Church."

Tyndale said thoughtfully, "There has always been a certain amount of persecution, even in England, since the time of John Wycliffe, more than a hundred years ago. He, too, preached the reform of the clergy, and there are still many who read his words."

"Are those the people who are called the Lollards?" Buschius asked.

"Yes. Many of them are poor folk, for Wycliffe's words are better remembered by the poor than by the rich and powerful. But there are others, as well." He was thinking of Humphrey Monmouth, his merchant patron, who had shown him plainly when he had been in London that he had Lollard sympathies. "There have been drives against them in the past," he added.

Buschius shook his head. "This is something different. Since the arrest of Robert Barnes last year the picture in England has changed. Or so my correspondent tells me. He says that soon after that, when your

New Testaments began arriving in the country, the clergy were greatly disturbed."

"I know that," Tyndale said impatiently. "But what has happened to Bilney?"

"So far he has refused to recant, and so he is still in the Tower."

Tyndale began to pace back and forth. "This news has settled something in my own mind," he said at last. His lean face wore a frown of concentration, and he stopped to gaze intently into the flames. "It is time I left Germany and made my headquarters in Antwerp."

"Antwerp!" Buschius whirled about so that he could face his friend. "Now, that would be foolhardy indeed. Here you are safe, at least, to continue with your work. Did you not say you were writing a book?"

"I have finished it, and it is ready for the printer."

"Well, you see, that makes it all the more necessary for you to stay here. You can have it printed here, or in Worms, without any danger. But in Antwerp—why, they threw van Endhoven in prison merely for printing copies of your New Testament."

"I will find a printer," Tyndale said stubbornly.

"But Antwerp is a Catholic city in a Catholic country. All Lutheran beliefs are considered rank heresy! You will be in danger of your very life!"

Now that he had made the decision, Tyndale was calmer. He came back to the fire to sit beside his friend, and to explain his reasons.

"Yes, Antwerp is a Catholic city," he admitted, "but

even there the city fathers, for the sake of trade, are inclined to overlook the opinions of the aliens in their midst. They do not interfere unless it is absolutely necessary. It is such a large city—three times larger than London—and there are many, many foreigners. One more may very well go unmarked. It will not be too difficult to hide there, I am sure."

"But you *will* have to hide," Buschius said triumphantly.

"True enough. But my friends will find me safe hiding places. And I shall have many friends there. The English merchants who are financing me have their Continental headquarters there. It should not be too difficult to find a comfortable cloak of anonymity."

"But you will come back here sometimes?" Buschius asked, a note of sadness in his voice. In these troubled times, one never knew, when parting from a friend, if he would ever be seen again.

"I cannot promise it," Tyndale said. "But a part of my heart will always stay with you and all my other friends in Germany."

6. BAD NEWS

(1528)

RICHARD HERMAN STEERED Tyndale through the thronged streets with a sure hand upon his arm, while the newcomer stared about at the vast city of Antwerp. They had come from the quays, where he had marveled at the shipping, for hundreds of ships, both foreign and native, came and went daily at the port. Every country of the civilized world had mercantile representatives here, and the streets were a babel of sound, with strange tongues heard on every side.

Herman was one of the English merchants who was responsible for the importation into England of Tyndale's books. He was a citizen of Antwerp, a big, self-confident man who had prospered in his work. He was taking an obvious pleasure in showing Tyndale the glories of Antwerp.

"Next," he said, "I must show you the Exchange Building."

Tyndale scarcely heard him. As always, his interest

lay in the people around him, and he was carefully studying the seething crowds. He recognized the tall, blond Flemish men who had, obviously, come from the farming country, as well as the short, dark, muscular Walloons from the hills inland. And scattered among these were Italians from Genoa and Venice, Spaniards, Portuguese, Germans and Swiss, high-cheekboned Scandinavians, even swarthy, strangely clad men whom he took to be Turks.

"Since the river Zwyn silted up, and Bruges harbor can no longer accommodate large seagoing ships," Herman was saying when Tyndale's attention returned to his guide, "all commerce has centered upon Antwerp. Not only do we have an exchange of goods here, but of money as well. It is a rich city, Sir William."

Tyndale had to agree, although he had spied, on their way from the docks, the slums without which no city seemed able to exist—high, rickety buildings on narrow, filthy streets, breeding grounds for disease and crime. Yet the squares, paved and thronged with well-dressed people, displayed every evidence of wealth. Surely there should not be such poverty where there was also so much wealth. It was not right that people should starve among such riches.

The problem that Herman had on his mind, however, was quite different. "I have found you a lodging," he said, "and I hope you will be comfortable there. You can be sure I was careful when I went about it, for it would not do to have you living among people unfriendly to your work. But it is small."

Tyndale smiled. "So long as there is room for my books and me, and for a friend who might visit me, I shall be content," he said. "When I am settled in, I must begin looking for a printer for my new book, however, and that is where you can help me."

"I have the very man," Herman said decisively. "John Hoochstraten is his name, though I much doubt he will be willing to use it on the colophon." He laughed, a hearty, booming laugh, so that several people turned to stare at him. Tyndale caught his breath and turned away quickly. One of those men had looked disturbingly familiar, but he could not place the face or tag it with a name. Yet he knew instinctively that it was the face of one who did not wish him well. And he was sure the man had recognized him.

Herman did not seem to have noticed, and as the man did not follow them, Tyndale said nothing. Instead, he put his attention once more to Herman's words. "Since van Endhoven's arrest, you can imagine that not many printers are anxious to suffer fines, imprisonment, or worse by printing books that are suspect. Do not be surprised if he should use another name, and even the name of another city, in the printing of your book."

"It would be wise to be secret about it," Tyndale agreed. "There is such a hue and cry these days concerning any book not sponsored by the Roman Church."

Herman shook his head. "You would be astonished to learn the subterfuges we must use in the handling of them," he commented. "And every day matters grow more difficult for us in England. Bishop Tonstall is avid for victims in his diocese and in Oxford as well."

"Oxford!" Tyndale echoed. His beloved friend Frith was at Oxford, a canon of Cardinal's College. A hand seemed to clutch at his heart. "What did he do there?"

"They have taken Thomas Garrett into custody, I hear. He is one of the distributors of your New Testament."

"He was the only one?" It was hard even to get the words out.

"Several of the canons of the university were taken to London and thrown into prison." Herman hesitated a moment, then blurted out, "Your friend John Frith was one of them."

Tyndale grew so pale that Herman came to a halt. He stood quietly until Tyndale had regained his composure, then took his arm again. "I should not have told you so bluntly," he said with contrition.

"He is like a son to me," Tyndale murmured. "Is there no other word concerning him?"

"Not concerning Frith," Herman acknowledged, "but there is word about another friend of yours." He looked anxiously at his companion, as if to estimate his strength. "But I will tell you about that when we have reached your lodging."

"No, tell me now," Tyndale said, his voice once more calm and steady.

Herman heaved a mighty sigh. "How I wish I were not the one to do it," he said. "Bishop Tonstall has scoured London so well that his prisons are full. As always, the poor Lollards have come in for their share of persecution, but this time Tonstall has added many others—men of education and standing. Humphrey Monmouth is one of them."

Tyndale's eyes widened with shock. "Monmouth!" he echoed. "But he is rich—powerful. And, I thought, unsuspected."

"It would seem the whole population of London is suspect at this moment," Herman cried angrily. "Tonstall is after anyone who may have distributed, or even read, your translation of the New Testament."

"But Monmouth . . ." Tyndale could not go on. Monmouth had seemed like a rock to him, invincible, entrenched in wealth and power. "What is the charge against him?" he finally asked.

"Lutheranism, of course. And he is suspected of being one of those who supervise the importation and sale of your books. But, worst of all, he is accused of having harbored one William Tyndale."

Tyndale was forced to stop again. His breath came short and hard. These were heavy blows he had received today. When he went forward once more, he murmured, "And all because he was kind to me."

Herman did not seem to have heard him. "You can

imagine his distress. His very life is in danger, and he must fear that his business may be ruined."

"And what—what is the outcome?" Tyndale was almost afraid to ask.

"We have not heard. This much came only yesterday with one of the regular couriers." Herman turned into a narrow alleyway and stopped before the door of an old house. "This is where you will lodge, Sir William. You can trust your landlord with your life, and everyone in the building as well, for he is careful to take in only those who have the same religious leanings as himself. And, if you should ever need me, you will know where to find me."

John Hoochstraten of Antwerp printed Tyndale's new book, *The Parable of the Wicked Mammon,* that spring, but he printed it under the name of Hans Lufft, of the city of Marburg, so important was the need for secrecy.

Only a month or so before it went through the presses, Tyndale had word of a little volume of doggerel that had begun to circulate in England. It was called *Rede Me and Be Not Wroth,* and it had been written by Friar Roye and a friend, Jerome Barlow, and printed in Strassburg. In it Cardinal Wolsey was lampooned in most unmerciful fashion, as were other English prelates.

Unfortunately, almost as soon as he heard of this little book, Tyndale also heard that it was being at-

tributed to him as well as to Roye, and this angered
him so that he inserted a preface to his *Mammon* in
which he indignantly denied authorship of the booklet.

In his own book, Tyndale spoke with dignity upon
a theme that was important to him. He said: "Christ is
thine, and all his deeds are thy deeds. Christ is in thee,
and thou in him, knit together inseparably. Neither
canst thou be damned, except Christ be damned with
thee: neither can Christ be saved, except thou be saved
with him."

He emphasized that good works proceed only from
a good heart, and he spurned all those hypocritical
actions which were done for form or for appearance,
and which had no genuine good will behind them.

But while Tyndale was instructing his fellow men
to follow Christ's example, the high churchmen of
England were trying to find ways to destroy him. One
fine June day they met in Wolsey's palace to discuss
how this could be done. They rustled into the oak-
paneled room, their stiff silken robes rich with orna-
ment, their faces bare of all kindliness.

Bishop Tonstall was the angriest of the lot. He
leaned across the polished table toward Cardinal
Wolsey, tapping the wood softly with his finger. "This
man Tyndale must be silenced. He is depraved, vicious!
He is striving to tear down the very fabric of the
church!"

Wolsey was more moderate. "Perhaps not so much
depraved as misled," he said. "In the petition that

Humphrey Monmouth signed in your very presence, Tonstall, he has described the man." He beckoned to a secretary, who fumbled through some papers, then handed him one of them. Wolsey read from it.

"He says: 'I took him into my house for half a year; and there he lived like a good priest, as me thought. He studied most part of the day and of the night at his book, and he would eat but sodden meat by his good will. . . . I never saw him wear linen about him in the space he was with me.' Now, this does not sound like someone who is depraved or vicious."

Tonstall controlled his voice with an effort. He said, breathing hard, "I am not speaking of the man's personal living habits, Your Eminence, but of what he writes. I am speaking of the evil influence he exerts upon all who read him. He is leading them into pernicious beliefs through the cunning of his iniquity. And," he paused only briefly before he added, "and he cares not whom he besmirches. The truth is completely removed from him. He does not hesitate to slander great men—" He stopped, not daring to go further, but what he said had penetrated, for the cardinal was still writhing beneath the ridicule of Roye's rhymes.

Wolsey, believing that Tyndale was the real author of these rhymes, nodded in agreement. "But where to find him?" he asked. "I have had agents seeking for him, but with no success. Every report we have received has been contradictory. He is in Germany—he

is *not* in Germany. He is in the Lowlands—he is *not* in
the Lowlands. Where is he? How can we reach him?"

"He is in the Lowlands, of that I am positive," Tonstall said quickly. "One of my household was in Antwerp this spring, and swears he saw him there. As for
reaching him—you could do it, you have the power."
Tonstall was referring to the fact that Wolsey was
Chancellor of England, the most powerful man in the
state except the king himself. "You could write to
Hackett, your ambassador, and *demand* that the Princess Margaret deliver him into our hands. *She* should
have the means to discover his whereabouts."

"And Friar Roye, too," Wolsey added somberly, still
smarting under the doggerel.

"And Richard Herman, as well, while we are about
it," one of the other prelates put in suddenly. "He is
the English merchant of Antwerp who is behind much
of the distribution of these books."

Wolsey nodded again. "Very well, then. And when
we have them—"

He broke off, but Tonstall's gesture was expressive.
He closed his white fingers into a fist.

It was fortunate for Tyndale that the times were
poor for Wolsey's "demand"; there was war that year
between Margaret's nephew, Emperor Charles V, and
the Anglo-French alliance. Although Margaret did her
best to maintain trade relations with England, her gov-
ernment was in no mood to scour the city for three

men wanted in England. And so, for a few weeks, there was a certain physical peace for Tyndale.

But his heart was torn with worry for his friends. Frith was still in prison, and Tyndale fretted because he could think of no way to help him. One night, when he was visiting Richard Herman, he said, "I must find some means of effecting John's release. If it means that I must give myself up for him, I will do it."

Herman laid a restraining hand upon Tyndale's sleeve. "It is a good thing you have spoken to me, or you would have gone off to your death without another thought. Do you not realize that John Frith is too well thought of to meet the usual fate? Wolsey is a great admirer of that young man. He and his friends would do much to have his talents upon their side, and they will find some way of letting him go, you may depend upon it."

Somewhat consoled, Tyndale went back to his simple lodgings. Too disturbed to rest, he set to work on the new volume he was finishing. He was deeply engrossed when there was a faint tapping upon his door. When he opened, it was to find one of Herman's assistants. He let him in at once.

"They've taken my master," the man cried, trembling. "They've thrown him into prison!"

Tyndale was aghast. He had just left Herman, secure in his home. Herman was a man of some influence. Surely he might have escaped; surely he would have

had some warning of this, for there were always in-
formers willing to earn a gold piece or two.

He asked anxiously, "What are they holding him
for?" and hoped against hope that it was something
trifling.

"They say he is a heretic, and he will be tried for it.
They say he has been supporting the English heretics
here in Antwerp, and has been sending forbidden
books into England and fomenting rebellion against
the English king."

Tyndale paced up and down the small room. This
was catastrophe, unless . . . "How are his affairs?" he
asked, though he doubted if the man would know of
such matters.

But this was one of Herman's most trusted em-
ployees. He said swiftly, "They will not be able to find
anything—we've seen to that—although they were
searching every nook and cranny when I left to bring
you this news." He paused, and said with emphasis,
"He said to tell you that there was a warrant out for
you, too, and one for Friar Roye."

Tyndale sighed. He would have to move. He would
have to take another name, another disguise of some
sort. But he would not leave Antwerp at this time.
There was so much to be done. There were other Englishmen to be warned. He looked about him. As always,
his possessions were so few that the packing and moving of them was no problem. Only his books . . . his
precious books . . .

By the next day he was gone from that lodging, and so large was the city and so quietly had he lived that there was no suspicion that the studious man, who had paid well for his simple wants and who seldom walked abroad, was the object of a frenzied search.

The following month word came that three of Frith's fellow prisoners had died. Tyndale, imagining the most dire outcome for his friend, was startled shortly thereafter to learn that he had been released. He remembered Herman's words and took heart from them. Perhaps the authorities in England *did* wish to save Frith for their own purposes. It mattered not, so long as John was alive and well, for he knew quite certainly that Frith's beliefs were too deeply rooted to be disturbed by their arguments.

It was difficult for him to get word these days, for he had been forced to move several times within as many weeks. It was fortunate that the English merchant friends of Tyndale could keep well informed through their English friends; they, in turn, sent messages to Tyndale in one way or another. It was thus that he learned of Humphrey Monmouth's release.

One day he came back to his lodgings to discover a man waiting for him. For a moment, the new habit of wariness that he had had to adopt made him turn away, but the man ran after him, crying, "Master Tyndale! God keep you! I have been searching for you."

It was George Constantine, whom he had not seen

since his departure from Cambridge. Heavier, even smoother of face and manner, somewhat prosperous looking.

Constantine did not give him the chance to answer his greeting. "I have come to give my help in your great work," he said.

"It is a work that I find I do better alone," Tyndale said, smiling to make the refusal kinder.

"Not in the writing—I would not be so bold as to suggest such a thing," Constantine protested. "But in the work of seeing that your books reach the people of England."

"It is dangerous work," Tyndale warned him.

"That I know well, for I am just fled from England myself," Constantine told him. "And I've a mind to settle in Brabant and practice medicine for a while. But I wish, too, to have some part, however small, in the work of reform."

"You have fled from England?" It was this that had caught Tyndale's ear. "What news do you bring?"

Constantine sighed. "None of it good, except that— despite all hardships—there is a strong core of determined men still working within the country, and their numbers grow daily. Bilney is still in prison, for he refuses to recant, although they have begged him to. Many have been arrested. Some, like me, have escaped to the Continent."

Tyndale thought, How many of us have had to flee

our country? Yet, when I left, there were still no outward signs that this could happen, and so soon.

Constantine broke into his thoughts. "There is a great hue and cry over your New Testament, as you well know. Yet, despite the danger of persecution, it has brought more comfort to men than you would believe."

"But not to the churchmen," Tyndale said wryly.

"And there," Constantine said seriously, "I believe it is not the translation so much as what they fear will result from the reading of it. Those in power have not forgotten the Peasants' War in Germany. They say the common people rose because Luther had given them a Bible in their own tongue, and that this only led to crime and anarchy among the ignorant."

"How foolish," Tyndale began, but Constantine rushed on.

"It is not only the churchmen who think this, but the lords and men of substance, as well. Everything they have heard of the uprisings in Germany has been magnified in their minds, and they blame it all on Luther. They foresee the same thing in England should Luther's doctrines ever be allowed safe entrance, and they are afraid."

"But Luther did not support the peasants in their rebellions. He told them that he preached only *religious* freedom."

Constantine heaved an impatient sigh. "How can you reason with men who are hounded by fear? . . .

And who, no doubt, are none too easy in their consciences," he added.

"Perhaps," Tyndale said slowly, "I may do some good, then, with my new book, which I am having printed next month."

"I had heard you were working on one, but what is it about?"

"I have called it *The Obedience of a Christian Man*, and I have written that we must follow Christ's command to obey the civil powers and to leave all vengeance to God, who will act in his season."

"Now, that should set their fears at rest," Constantine said with satisfaction. "Perhaps, when they read that, they will moderate their stand concerning the Scriptures."

Tyndale, for answer, picked up a copy of his *Mammon*, and riffled through the pages before he laid it down again. "In this book," he said sadly, "I preached 'Love thy neighbor' again and again. Yet it seems to have small effect upon men in power, for it has been sought out and burned wherever possible."

"How far the world has come from Christ's teaching," Constantine cried, "when such things can be!"

"Yes, it is a thought to sadden one," Tyndale replied. "But it is also a spur to further effort."

Tyndale's new book, which John Hoochstraten printed for him that October with great secrecy, was sharper in tone than his previous works, for it reflected many things that had hurt him: the persecution of his friends and the degeneration of the clergy, among others.

There was, too, a reflection of those things he had seen and heard in England when he said: "Let Christian landlords be content with their rent and old customs, not raising rent or fines, and bringing up new customs to oppress their tenants. . . . Let them not take in their commons, neither make parks nor pastures of whole parishes: for God gave the earth to man to inherit, and not unto sheep and wild deer."

He had, as he told Constantine, instructed men to "obey the civil powers," and he had supported the "divine right of kings." But he had also said that "though kings are supreme, they may not rule as they list. They are servants of their people, and must treat every man, no matter how humble, as a brother."

He was walking home one day from Hoochstraten's printing shop when one of his English merchant friends spied him. "Sir William! Now, this is well-met, indeed. You must come with me, for I have a surprise for you that will warm your heart."

Tyndale looked at him. "They have released Herman?"

The other sobered. "No, not yet, although it appears they will have to in the end, for they have no evidence against him."

The merchant took Tyndale's arm and guided him down a narrow, crooked alleyway. He knocked at the

door of a small, leaning house with shuttered windows.
It looked unoccupied. Perhaps it was a warehouse of
some sort, Tyndale thought, and the man was bringing
him here so they could talk unobserved. Yet he had
said "a surprise."

When they were inside the dark hallway and the
door had closed behind them, someone came forward
with a light. The wavering flame disclosed a face familiar and dear to Tyndale.

"John!" he cried. The light was set down hurriedly,
and he was clasped in the strong arms of his young
friend, John Frith.

"How do you come here?" he demanded when his
first emotion had subsided and he could speak in his
natural voice. "When last I heard, you had just been
released from the Tower."

Frith laughed, and his handsome face turned to his
friend eagerly. "It was Wolsey got me out."

"Wolsey!" This could scarcely be believed. But, of
course, Frith was one of the young men Wolsey had
taken from Cambridge to grace his new Cardinal's
College at Oxford. Frith was, really, a protégé of
Wolsey's.

"He got me out of prison," Frith chuckled, "and I
was told I must not go farther than ten miles from
Oxford. But it's a stupid beast who stays in the trap
when the door is left open."

"And so you fled—like so many others," Tyndale said
thoughtfully.

"It was that or give up all that I hold dear. It was that or live a lie forever more," Frith cried in justification. "It was that or give myself up to mumbo-jumbo from now on, with never a thought of my own!"

Tyndale put a gentle hand upon his arm. "No, never think that I would have had it otherwise," he said quietly. "I was only wondering how many there will be left in England to enlighten the people."

"More than you think," Frith cried eagerly. "The Merchant Adventurers have a masterly organization for the distribution of books, and your translation of the New Testament has reached many folk who were thirsting for it. They, in turn, have shared their good fortune with others of like mind, so that it spreads and spreads. It is no wonder the churchmen are worried."

He threw back his head with a laugh. "And how they have been writhing under your *Mammon!* There have been more conclaves, and refutations, and fine words twisted about than you would believe possible. As for your new book, *The Obedience of a Christian Man,* there you have hobbled them well! I've even heard that King Henry finds it a rod to strengthen him. For Henry is a determined man, and Wolsey's power has become too all-enveloping for his taste."

Tyndale nodded. "Then he has seen a copy?"

"They say he has and that he found much he liked in it."

Tyndale nodded again. "That he may, at this time. But I shall not be surprised if later he finds much that displeases him as well. People often see only what they wish to see when they read."

"You mean that he will sometime find the preface not to his liking?" Frith said. "How could he? It is so clear, so just. It explains so simply why we should have an English Bible." And he quoted softly, " 'They say our tongue is too rude. It is not so. Greek and Hebrew go more easily into English than into Latin. Has not God made the English tongue as well as the others? They suffer you to read in English of Robin Hood, Bevis of Hampton, Hercules, Troilus, and a thousand ribald and filthy tales. It is only the Scripture that is forbidden.' "

He broke off and said, smiling, "I have had much time for reading lately, and my friends have brought me your book. I think I could recite most of it to you."

7. SHIPWRECK AND PURSUIT
(1529-1531)

TYNDALE HAD BEGUN his translation of the Old Testament in Worms, and throughout his stay in Germany and later when he had moved to Antwerp, he had continued with it despite his work on *Mammon* and *Obedience* and the necessity of overseeing their printing and distribution. By the early part of 1529 he felt that the Pentateuch, the first five books of the Old Testament, was ready for the press.

And now a problem came to plague him. Although he preferred to stay in Antwerp, where he was close to England and where the Merchant Adventurers lent him a small amount of protection, he was in constant danger. Spies from England, as well as agents of the regent, were always on his track. In January his name was mentioned in open court as a heretic and rebel, and when Richard Herman was finally released in February, he gravely informed Tyndale that to print the Pentateuch in Antwerp at this time was to endanger himself as well as the printer.

"But where can I go?" Tyndale cried. "The men who are hunting me are scattered throughout those parts of Germany where I formerly lived. They are covering the Frankfort book fairs. I must find *some* place where I can have the translation printed!"

It was Frith who suggested the answer. "Why not Hamburg? The city is no longer in the hands of the papal party. You would be safe there."

Tyndale considered this. But Herman spoke at once. "The Merchant Adventurers have a branch there."

"And," Frith continued, "have I not heard that Richolff the younger, of the famous printing house of Lübeck, has recently settled in Hamburg? He would be your man. Even if the report were false, you would not be far from Lübeck itself. You could have the printing done there."

It was a good solution, Tyndale felt. If only he had not had to part from this dear friend after having been so recently reunited with him! But he could not allow his personal feelings to stand in the way of his work. He never had, and he never would, he knew. "I shall need someone to help me," he said.

Frith had a solution for this problem, too. "Why not Miles Coverdale? You know he helped Robert Barnes prepare his defense. That was bad enough, I imagine, but lately he has been in trouble for preaching against confession and the worship of images."

"Very well," Tyndale agreed. "I shall go to Hamburg, then."

It was arranged; and Tyndale, together with his books and papers and, above all, his precious translation, went down to the harbor one winter's day and took ship. His friends came with him, to make sure he was comfortable, and he was touched by their parting gifts of food.

He stowed his things below decks—all but the manuscript, which he had wrapped in an oiled cloth so that the sea spray would not harm it. That he carried with him everywhere. Frith teased him about it a little before he returned to the quay. "The captain will be sure you have robbed a wealthy burgher of his gold and jewels, the way you clutch that parcel to you," he laughed. Then he sobered, "It is not an auspicious day for sailing," he added. "I can feel a storm in the air."

Tyndale agreed. It was raw and blustery, and the wind stung like whips. He watched the figure of his friend dwindle away to a mere speck before he moved away from the rail, and then, observant as always, turned his attention to the seamen as they clambered up the mast or coiled ropes in neat piles. Perhaps, he thought suddenly, he had been foolish not to make the trip overland.

His misgivings grew to a certainty when they left the harbor and the storm caught at the little ship, tossing it about as if it were made of straw. There were few passengers, and these were huddled below in a trance of fear. The wind whistled through the rigging with an eerie sound, and the roar of the storm was like thunder.

Tyndale would have liked to stay on deck, but the captain ordered him below with the others. "Are you going to head through it?" he asked before he left.

The captain's squat figure almost disappeared in a sudden gust of rain and spray. His thick beard was blown to one side with the force of the wind. Even the gleam of his gold earring was dulled by the darkness. He said, "I dare not. I'll try to stay within sight of shore."

Tyndale's glance to starboard was eloquent. "We cannot see it even now," he said, but the other did not answer.

It was hours later that he sensed a change in the storm. Or was it a change in the ship? He did not know. The poor thing answered sluggishly enough to the helm at all times, but now there was a wildness in her movements. She seemed at times almost to fly upon the crest of a gigantic wave, only to shudder helplessly a moment later in the trough. Orders or no, he had to know what was happening.

At that very moment, the captain's bellow reached them. "All hands on deck! We're being driven ashore!"

The men beside Tyndale reached with panicky fingers for their belongings. One merchant, groaning over a shipment of tapestry, and unable to decide what to save, was suddenly thrown from his feet.

"We've struck!" someone cried, and there was a rush for the companionway.

Tyndale followed them. His books, his clothing, the gifts of his friends, were left behind without a backward glance. He clutched the parcel of his manuscript closely. What good fortune that he had it so carefully wrapped!

It was the last coherent thought he had for a long time, for he was swept from his feet, whirled about in a froth of water that pounded him, twisted him, threw him about. How could he swim with his arms filled? But he would not let go . . . he would not let go . . .

When he opened his eyes, he gazed about him for a moment in pure puzzlement. Where was he, and what had happened? And then the memory of those last frantic struggles came to him, and he tried to sit upright.

A fisherman's wife came over to the bed and pushed him down again. "Now, now," she said in Dutch, "back under the covers with you! I've had enough trouble bringing you back to life to have you leaving it again."

He had only one thought. "My bundle. Where is it?"

She shook her head, smiling at him in a pitying fashion. "Bundle!" she echoed. "You'd not a stitch on you when my good man fetched you out of the sea, much less anything like a bundle."

Tyndale lay for a long while, digesting this. He had nothing—nothing at all. The jealous sea had not only ripped the clothes from his body; it had torn from him a very part of his life. Months and months of work had gone into that translation, and now it was gone.

The woman seemed to sense what he was feeling, but she misinterpreted it. "You must not despair, man. What if you have lost all you possess? You're alive, aren't you?"

It was useless to tell her that his despair was not for himself. He knew that once he had sent word to his friends in Antwerp they would dispatch money and clothing and everything needful. But they could not replace the long, careful work that had gone into his translation.

No one could replace that, he thought mournfully. And then he thought, no one but myself.

At that he straightened and his eyes brightened. After all, as the woman had said, was he not still alive? Did he not still possess the knowledge for the task? And perhaps—perhaps he could make a *better* translation this time!

Money and clothing and books arrived in due course. Tyndale rewarded his rescuers and took another ship for Hamburg. No longer daunted by the prospect of the work ahead, he came safely to the German port and set forth at once to find the house of the Widow von Emersen, where he had lodged five years before.

It was good to find a familiar place and familiar faces. The house still stood upon the Huxter; the Widow von Emersen still kept it clean and shining. She welcomed him kindly and was willing that Miles

Coverdale—who had eagerly accepted the invitation to work with him—should lodge there.

The two men plunged into their work. There was so much time to be made up—valuable months that had been washed away by the sea.

Miles Coverdale was a well-educated man, and his services were invaluable in the necessary comparison of various versions of the Pentateuch and in the correction of the copies that Tyndale proceeded to make.

The translation was still fresh in Tyndale's mind. It did not take him long to write out a new one when he had the necessary books at hand, although, as always, he searched every word anew to make sure he had made the best and truest translation that he could.

It was not many months before the work was ready for the printer. Only now, in this short time, matters had changed so greatly that he no longer need have it printed here in Hamburg. He could go back to Antwerp and put it in the hands of Hoochstraten, as he had originally planned. This he did in 1530.

In these months of Tyndale's labor, Wolsey, the magnificent, the rival of kings, had fallen. Henry VIII, determined to rid himself of his first wife so that he might marry Anne Boleyn, was threatening the universities of Oxford and Cambridge in order to get them to pronounce in his favor against the pope, who had refused the divorce, and he had sent emissaries to Europe to canvass the European universities as well—

emissaries who were using any means, including presents, in order to get the verdict he desired.

So much was happening at home in England that the pursuit of men like Tyndale had been abandoned for the time being. He would be as safe in Antwerp as anywhere, he told himself, and although his friends protested that Germany would be far safer, he wished to be where he could meet his refugee friends as they fled to the Continent and where he could oversee the battle that his books had initiated.

The Pentateuch, when it appeared later in England, brought down the wrath of the authorities upon his head even more violently than before. This was not only because of his boldness in persisting in his intention to bring the Bible before the common folk of England, but especially because of the glosses that it contained.

Glosses are comments which a translator makes in the margin of a book, usually for the purpose of explaining some obscure word or phrase. But Tyndale did not stop there. Time and again he employed the glosses for sharp comment upon the church and its practices, upon the pope and his prelates. It was these glosses that brought the great ones of the Roman Church together in a mighty, condemnatory union against him.

Two years before, Bishop Tonstall had urged his friend, Sir Thomas More, a famed scholar and an eminent Catholic, to write a refutation of Tyndale's theses. The refutation, named *Dialogue* from the form in which it was written, was a vicious and slanderous attack upon Tyndale and his work.

More said that Tyndale was "so puffed up with . . . pride, malice, and envy, that it is more than a marvel that the skin can hold together." And he claimed that Tyndale had willfully mistranslated the Scripture and deceived uneducated people by teaching what he knew to be false.

The *Dialogue* appeared in June, 1529, and Tyndale was moved to make a reply. But even if he had been willing to pass over the book in silence, his friends would not have permitted it. John Frith was especially indignant.

"I shall answer him myself!" he cried, striding up and down his room in the heat of his anger. He was thoroughly aroused. "I shall make him eat his words!"

"Would you poison the man?" Tyndale inquired with gentle irony.

"Is the serpent poisoned by his own venom?" Frith shot back.

"I am inclined to ignore his *Dialogue*," Tyndale said with more firmness, seeing how upset his young friend was. "That would be a worse hurt to the man than any reply we could make."

"I am not thinking only of More's *words*," Frith said, coming to a halt before his friend and looking at him with compelling gaze. "I am thinking of the reputation

he has among men of learning and letters; of his position, for since Wolsey's fall he is the king's Chancellor;
of his standing with his royal master; of the way in
which everything he says will be swallowed by the
people unless it is refuted."

This last argument was the only one that made an
impression upon Tyndale. "Perhaps you are right," he
conceded at last. "Perhaps we should make a reply to
him."

Frith caught at his shoulders. "Let me help you," he
begged. "Oh, I can think of so *many* things to say.
Here," he whipped about to the small table where ink-
horn and quill were laid, "where is my paper? Let us
start now."

While he and Tyndale began to compose the reply
to Sir Thomas More, the churchmen in England made
another move against religious reform. They petitioned
King Henry to scotch the rumors that he was in favor
of permitting the Bible to circulate among the people
in their own language. They asked him to make a
proclamation against it. Perhaps their worry was
brought to a climax when they learned that Henry had
found some things to his liking in Tyndale's *Obedience*
——in those portions, at least, which claimed that the
Roman Church had usurped too many civil rights and
duties.

A good deal of pressure was brought to bear upon
the king and he did, in May, 1530, declare against
Tyndale's books. He also denied that there was any

need for an English version of the Scriptures *at the present*. And then Henry promised that in due course such a translation would be available to the public, but that it would be made by the proper people, "great, learned and Catholic persons."

Bishop Tonstall had only recently returned from Europe. On his way back to England he had stopped briefly in the Low Countries, and there he had managed to buy up a great many of Tyndale's books by one means or another. These he now burnt at St. Paul's Cross, making as much of a spectacle of it as he could.

In March, Tyndale's old friend and ally, Thomas Hitton, had been sent to the stake at Maidstone. But men like Hitton were not prominent enough in the reformed cause to satisfy the men who were trying to crush Lutheranism in England. They desired more than anything else to have in their power the man whom they considered the leader, the "captain of heretics," as he was called—Tyndale.

To this end they were unwittingly helped by Thomas Cromwell, the king's secretary. But Cromwell had quite a different aim in mind, one that would have dismayed Tyndale's enemies had they known it.

Finding his royal master in a good mood one day, Cromwell brought up the subject. "Have you ever thought, Sire," he asked, "what a pen so persuasive as Master Tyndale's could do for us if it were to be employed *by* us instead of against us?"

Henry, lolling back in a large oaken chair with sapphire velvet cushions, studied Cromwell through slitted eyes. "Now, what devious schemes are being unraveled in your brain, Thomas?" he demanded. "The man Tyndale is obnoxious to me, and you know it well. In his new book—what is it called—"

"*The Practice of Prelates*," Cromwell said instantly.

"Yes. Well, in that book he has offended me beyond repair. Did he not, in that very book, have the effrontery to oppose my divorce? Pah! Even the hardiest Lutheran reformers here in England have not done so."

Cromwell said swiftly, "Perhaps because they prefer to differ with any and all of the pope's pronouncements."

"No matter why," the king cried testily, "they are for it, and he is not. Who is he to put himself against his king's wishes?"

Cromwell said, one anxious eye on his monarch, "I believe, Sire, it was not only the religious angle which concerned him, but the political one, as well."

"And what business has a whining heretic to deal with politics? The man's overbold." He leaned forward a little. "*What* did he say about the political angle?"

Cromwell wished that he had never started this discussion, but he kept his expression bland and unworried. "Why, he felt it would make for uncertainty concerning the succession should Your Majesty be blessed with children by the new marriage. And that this could easily lead to civil war, or foreign invasion, or even to the murder of rivals."

The king digested this in silence for a moment. Then he said, "The fool! Did I not order placards set out in prominent places, telling the people that the universities had declared in favor of my divorce? And was not this same Tyndale's book mentioned by name in the placards—in a condemnatory fashion?" He heaved himself a little straighter in the chair and bent the full force of his stare upon the secretary. "You *have* put out those placards, as I ordered?"

"Certainly, Your Majesty. I would not have dreamed of disobeying," Cromwell hastened to answer. "Not only that, but Tyndale's own brother, John, was arrested last month, with other Lutheran merchants, and made to ride through the streets of London in most humiliating fashion—backwards upon horses, with copies of the New Testament and other of William Tyndale's books pinned to their clothing. The people made good sport of them."

The king grunted. "They were fined, too, I hope."

"Certainly, Sire."

"Then why this sudden desire on your part to befriend the author of these condemned books?"

"I did not mean to befriend him, Sire, but to employ him to your benefit."

"What do you mean?"

"I mean," Cromwell spoke slowly, and chose his words with care, "that if this man were properly approached, and made to feel that he would be forgiven, he could turn the power of his pen to *your* causes. For there is no denying, Your Majesty, that his pen has power. Men read his words avidly, whenever they can come by them, and he has the gift of convincing the most reluctant reader. Now, if that power were engaged in *your* employ—"

"I see, I see," the king cried testily. He never liked to be convinced against his will, yet he had to admit that the wily secretary had made an interesting proposal. "But how would we win him to us? How persuade him to come back to England? I understand," there was a twinkle suddenly in his narrowed eyes, "that Wolsey had no success at it, nor has Tonstall, nor any of the other churchmen who have tried to lay their hands on him."

"And with good reason. He knew that they meant him harm, and so he has eluded them. But if he were approached by one whom he felt he could trust . . ."

"Come, man, name him. You must have someone particular in mind!"

"I do, indeed. I was thinking of Stephen Vaughan of the Merchant Adventurers in Antwerp."

"The man you have been pressing me to make my factor in the Low Countries?" Henry asked.

"Yes, Your Majesty."

The king seemed to make up his mind suddenly. "Very well, see to it. We should wish him to persuade John Frith, as well. And we might as well make Vaughan our factor—thus he will have more authority."

Cromwell was pleased. But he was too wise to show

his pleasure. He only said, "I think there is some chance of success in this venture since Emperor Charles put forth his strict edict."

"Which one?" Henry asked drily.

"The one, last year, in which he ordered all New Testaments, in whatever language, surrendered and destroyed, all printing of such books forbidden, and all heretics put to death. Such dire conditions may well make Master Tyndale more anxious to return to the healthier climate of England, Sire."

The king rose to his feet and moved toward the door of the room where they had been talking. Cromwell made haste to reach the door before him and to hold it open, bowing low. "It might be as well," Henry said casually as he left, "to have those placards removed, after all. If we are going to send Vaughan to persuade him to return."

Now, Vaughan was not in close touch with the reformers of Antwerp, and his assignment in this matter was not an easy one, for he had no true information concerning the whereabouts of Tyndale. At first he sent forth three letters, hoping that one of them might reach the man he sought. He sent one to Hamburg, one to Frankfort, and one to Marburg. Gossip had it that Tyndale had recently written a book in answer to Sir Thomas More and that he might be in one of those places in order to have it printed.

Tyndale was, of course, in Antwerp all this time, but he was too wary to disclose his presence to anyone who asked for him. Every letter from England made clearer the danger that surrounded his friends who were distributing his books. He would have been a blind fool if he had not been aware of what awaited the *author* of those books in England.

And then, one April day, Stephen Vaughan's servant came to him to say that a poor man wished to speak with him. Vaughan was curious, thinking that perhaps some of his inquiries might at last be bearing fruit, and he went out to speak to the stranger.

The man said, with an air of reciting a string of memorized words, "A certain friend of yours, unknown to me, wishes to speak with you. He begs you to come with me."

Vaughan was puzzled. "Who is this friend, and where is he?"

But the man answered, "I do not know his name, but if you wish to go where he is, I will be glad to bring you there."

Vaughan hesitated only briefly. The mystery seemed to indicate that here at last was someone who was willing to give him information concerning Tyndale. He caught up his cloak and hat and followed the messenger through the twisting streets, through the city gate, and out into a field nearby.

A man rose from his seat on the ground beneath a spreading tree and came toward him. A man whose high forehead, steady gaze, and quiet clothing marked him for a scholar. He wore, too, such an air of innate dignity that Vaughan approached him with sober respect.

When he was face to face with the other man, he stopped, not knowing what to say, and the other, after a moment's gaze into his eyes, said, "Do you not know me?"

Vaughan was troubled. Surely, if he had ever met this man before, he would not have forgotten him. "I do not well remember you," he answered hesitantly.

"My name is Tyndale."

Vaughan was really startled. Could this man whose face radiated high purpose, whose steady eyes surveyed the world with calmness and even pity, could this be the hunted leader of the English heretics?

They talked together then, and Tyndale explained his position and the reasons for it. He said, speaking of his latest book, *The Practice of Prelates*, "I have felt it my duty, as an Englishman, to warn the king and my fellow countrymen of the dangers that threaten our country. Not the least of these has been the subtle and continuous encroachment of the Roman Church upon the civil rights and duties of the authorities, who could, in some instances, no longer act as they should. I have wished to tell them of the danger in which they stand."

Vaughan sighed. "But, Sir William, you must know that such warnings are not received kindly either by the ones who offend or by the ones who are offended against."

"Still, I should be doing less than my duty if I did

not give them," Tyndale cried. "And events are proving me right. The king did at last see that Cardinal Wolsey was gathering all power into his hands, and brought about his downfall."

Vaughan saw his chance. "The king's eyes are opened. You may be sure of that," he told Tyndale, "and now he wishes you to return to your native country."

Tyndale said cautiously, "Would he permit the Bible to be translated into English and to be circulated freely among the people?"

Vaughan, not daring to answer this affirmatively, shifted to another plea. "He offers you a safe-conduct. You need have no fear, Sir William."

Tyndale shook his head. "Even the king's safe-conduct might be of little use to me," he said sadly, "for I am quite sure the clergy would succeed in persuading him that it should be broken. They have said before that promises made to heretics ought not to be kept. And they call me a heretic."

It was growing dark when at last Tyndale said, "I must leave you now. Perhaps you will see me again, or at least hear from me." And he walked rapidly away from the city, while Stephen Vaughan returned to his lodgings in a bemused state of mind.

He wrote to the king, and so much of his involuntary respect and admiration for Tyndale crept into the letter that the king became angry. Cromwell wrote his friend that he should make no further effort to induce Tyndale to return to England, but he requested Vaughan to continue his efforts with John Frith, for him they had hopes of recalling "to the right way."

By the time Vaughan had this letter, Frith was in Holland and had married there. Besides, Vaughan himself was so interested in Tyndale that he was loath to give up the chance to befriend him.

When they met again, Tyndale said, "I assure you, if only the king would permit an English Bible to be given to the people—no matter who the translator might be—I would promise to write nothing more."

Vaughan thought that this was nearly victory, but there was more, for Tyndale added, "And if this should happen, I would then return at once to England of my free will, there to submit myself to the king, willing to take pain, or torture, or even death if my sovereign wishes it."

"Now, surely, there would be nothing like that demanded of you," Vaughan hastened to say.

But Tyndale said firmly. "It might be. And I would not begrudge it, for then my task would be accomplished. My countrymen would have the Scripture in their own tongue."

This was his condition and his only one, but it was a condition Vaughan was sure King Henry would not accept. Nor could Vaughan move him from it. It seems, from his letters, that he was so admiring of Tyndale that he did not really try.

This was the last attempt that was made to *persuade*

Tyndale to return to England. After this try the authorities would use harsher measures, and Tyndale knew it. But he neither could, nor would, change his tune. He meant Englishmen to have their own Scripture, and nothing would turn him from his resolve.

8. UNDAUNTED FUGITIVE

(1531-1535)

AND NOW CAME FEARFUL NEWS to the little band of refugees on the Continent. Friend after friend in England was seized, imprisoned, questioned. Some who had been arrested before, and who had recanted to save their lives, were ashamed of their first weakening and began working once more for the cause of reform.

Among them was Little Bilney. Three years before he had spent a year in the Tower for his beliefs. At last he had recanted and had been released to return to Cambridge. But he was a broken man. His friends had worried. His despair was so great that many times they feared he would take his own life.

At last, after two years of self-reproach, he had made up his mind to live as he felt right, and he went forth once more to preach ardently to the people. He came, in the end, to Norwich, and there he presented an anchoress with Tyndale's New Testament and his *Obedience*.

From that moment he was a doomed man. Word came to the Continent that he had been burned at Norwich in August, and there was real mourning among those who had known him.

Little Bilney was not the only one. The aroused authorities were spying out every one they could, and the importation of books from Antwerp became increasingly dangerous—and increasingly important. Many of Tyndale's friends were captured.

The final blow was Constantine's arrest. Active in the work of distributing books ever since he had asked Tyndale to let him help in it, Constantine was discovered on one of his trips to England and imprisoned in the house of Sir Thomas More, where he was questioned. Cruelly chained and fearful of the torture, he broke and gave his captors much valuable information. Through his confession they were able to intercept a large shipment of books, for he had not only given them the names of the handlers but had even told More's men how to recognize the particular bundles that would contain books by the special markings on them.

Eventually Constantine managed to escape, and he fled back to Antwerp. His once full cheeks were hollow and pale and his eyes were furtive; for now not only was he a hunted man in England, but he had betrayed his friends abroad. He came to Tyndale almost at once and broke into a long explanation of why he had been so cowardly.

Tyndale heard him out, for he sensed that the man was in mental agony. When at last Constantine ceased to speak and sat silent with his head bowed, as if inviting Tyndale's condemnation, he said, "You have done so much to advance our cause, Constantine, and have walked in danger many times. Why do you berate yourself for your one act of weakness? Do we not all have our moments of despair, moments when we yield to fear? If you must make a balance of your life's deeds, will you not find that the good outweighs the bad a hundredfold?"

Constantine raised his head, hardly daring to believe what he had heard. "It was not only myself," he muttered, still shamefaced. "It was thinking of my wife over here, and what might befall her . . . but I did not stop to think enough of those others whom I betrayed."

Tyndale shook his head. "There has been harm done and I would not have you deny it to yourself. But the loss of some books and the payment of some fines are small matters compared to what you have done and what you still can do."

When Constantine left him some time later, his head once more erect upon his shoulders, Tyndale sighed. This was a business truly to try men's souls. He thought to himself that, firm as he was in his beliefs, the temptation to weaken might well be overwhelming if he had wife and children. The life he led was a lonely one, but it was the only life for one who had dedicated himself to such dangerous work.

He thought of what he had learned that morning. Sir Thomas Elyot, the new ambassador to the Low Countries, had made a strong demand for Tyndale to the authorities. But since the authorities, being representative of the emperor's state of mind, were infuriated by Henry VIII's defiance of the church in the matter of his divorce, there was small chance of their agreeing to the demand.

Perhaps Elyot had sensed this, for now he was trying to find Tyndale's whereabouts by means of bribery. In such a city as Antwerp there were many homes that were open to Tyndale for refuge and concealment. But there were many more folk who would have counted it a privilege to betray him to his countrymen. It was the task of his friends among the Lowlanders to keep alert to every move that Elyot made, to know where every bribe was placed, and to offset any information that Elyot might receive by a move of their own.

For the past year Tyndale had seldom been in the same place for more than a few weeks at a time. And this constant shifting of his residence and his few possessions was not only tiring but disconcerting.

It interfered, too, with his custom of using Mondays for looking up those English refugees who might be in want and relieving their needs in his quiet fashion, comforting them when he could and teaching them how to live in a strange country. Sometimes he was able to find employment for them, and that was the best of all, for any man who was occupied had little time for despair.

He did not confine his charitable efforts only to his own people, but searched out all those who lived in need in the crowded warrens of the Antwerp slums. For these he spent his Saturdays and all the money he could spare.

It was often from these people that he received timely warning of some move to be made against him, for their ragged urchins sped easily about the city, and word spread quickly among them. Yet it was not for their warnings that he helped them, but because he truly loved them and pitied them.

By June, 1532, Elyot had his fill of the game and resigned his post to return to England, decidedly out of pocket from all his attempts to buy information concerning Tyndale. But it was impossible, from this time forth, for Tyndale to live openly. He never knew when some new attempt might be made to seize him, and he continued to abide quietly in inconspicuous places.

In July, Frith went to England, a foolhardy thing to do. But he was confident that he could make the trip undetected. Only the year before he had made a quick journey into his homeland and had returned safely.

But no sooner had Frith reached Reading, where he had business with a prior of Lutheran convictions, than he was arrested as a suspicious stranger. Wisely he refused to give his name, but this brought upon him

a charge of vagrancy and a sentence to the stocks.
Finally, weak with hunger and exhaustion, he took advantage of an old law that excused educated men from
common punishment. A display of his knowledge to
the local schoolmaster brought freedom, but he escaped
from the stocks only to find that the English authorities
had learned of his presence in England and were in
full cry after him and the prior, who had fled from
Reading with him.

Changing their hiding places and their clothing time
and again, avoiding the highroads and moving secretly
by night, the two hunted men evaded the furious pursuit until October, when they were caught and imprisoned in the Tower.

Tyndale's heart sank when the news was brought to
him. Only too well did he know John Frith to be a
headstrong young man, and uncommonly brave into
the bargain—one who would never avoid danger to
save himself, one who would speak out even if it meant
his death.

He spoke of his worries to Thomas Poyntz, a member of the grocers' company and distantly related to
Lady Walsh of Little Sodbury. Poyntz was his friend
and tried to cheer him by saying, "Now, it is well
known, Sir William, how young Frith is esteemed by
many of the great in England. If there is any way at
all that they can get him out of this danger, they will
do so, never fear. Why, there is Gardiner, his old
tutor—surely he would wish no harm to him. And even

Sir Thomas More is more kindly disposed toward Frith than toward any other of our faith that I know of."

Tyndale sat silent. He wished to believe this; he knew well that there had been many efforts to draw Frith back into the fold of the church, for his learning and charm were vastly desired in the Roman Catholic ranks. Yet he could not shake off the sense of foreboding.

He said, "It is John himself that I fear. He is so eager for argument. I am afraid he may make some move that the authorities will not be able to overlook, that he will doom himself."

Poyntz sighed. He knew how devoted Frith had been to Tyndale, how greatly Tyndale loved the young man. He said hesitantly, "Perhaps if you wrote him thus, it would keep him from making any foolhardy move. And if you should write him, I think we may be able to smuggle the letter in to him. But do not address him by his rightful name. If it should be discovered that he receives letters of advice from the 'captain of heretics,' he would be in grave danger."

Tyndale brightened at that. He crossed the room to his writing table and sat down. "Dearly beloved brother Jacob," he wrote, "mine heart's desire in our Saviour Jesus is, that you arm yourself with patience, and be cold, sober, wise, and circumspect; and that you keep a-low by the ground, avoiding high questions that pass the common capacity. . . ."

The words flowed from his pen. He felt himself in

communication with his dear friend. If only John would not allow himself to be drawn into any arguments, all might yet be well.

Tyndale's letter of caution came too late. Frith had already begun his heretical writings, and then, to settle the matter, the king was prodded into moving against him. Cromwell and Archbishop Cranmer—friendly as they were toward the young man—had no choice after that but to bring him to trial. But an attempt was made to save him in such a way that it would seem to have happened by accident.

Cranmer sent one of his gentlemen and a porter to escort Frith to his palace at Croydon for examination, and on the way the gentleman drew Frith aside.

"If you are wise, Sir John," he said, "you will not speak boldly before the archbishop, who is well disposed toward you and who would gladly find some way of excusing you if he might."

"I can only say what I believe," Frith replied, throwing his head back with a defiant gesture.

"But need you say anything at all?" the man continued. "Why condemn yourself out of your own mouth? Why not think of your wife and young children, who will be widowed and orphaned so soon if you persist in your present ways?"

Frith bit his lip, for he had been touched on a tender place. "They will understand," he murmured.

The gentleman, seeing his advantage, went further.

"Better to be silent now, too," he added, "for the sake of what you believe to be the truth, for if you are wise you will live to preach it later."

But at that Frith shook his head. "One cannot deny the truth and then preach it," he said with unshakable firmness. "What man believes a thief to be honest, or a liar to tell the truth? And that is what I should be if I denied my beliefs now—a liar." He saw that the other man was about to argue further, and he said quickly, "If I had twenty lives, I would give them all, for only in that way will the truth prevail. In a score of years, I will wager the greater part of England will take my side of the matter."

The gentleman was silent, and when they had reached Lambeth and had their meal there, they went on foot toward Croydon. For a while he spoke with the Welsh porter, and then suddenly he spoke again to Frith.

"Look you," he said, "when we are near Brixton, there is a place where you could slip away into the woods at the left-hand side of the road, and make for Kent where you were born and where you would have friends to hide you."

Frith was startled. "But you would be putting your own heads into the noose," he protested.

"No, for we will raise a hue and cry, never fear. Only we will be searching the *right-hand* side of the road."

Frith, who had once said that "it is a stupid beast that stays in the trap when the door is open," did not even consider the plan. He said firmly, "If you should both leave me here and go to Croydon declaring to the bishops that you had lost me, I would follow after you as fast as possible and bring them the news that I had been found again."

"But why should you refuse your liberty now," the gentleman cried, "when, six months ago, you strained every nerve to escape the country?"

"Six months ago," Frith answered, "I was a free man and had no need to run into danger. Now I am face to face with my enemies, and I must not now refuse to testify to my faith, and so betray the cause of God."

He was as good as his word. Steadfastly refusing to recant and sturdily holding to his beliefs, he sealed his fate. News of his brave death by burning came to Tyndale at Antwerp in July, a year after Frith had left him to go to England. It was a bitter blow, for he had loved the young man like a son.

But Tyndale's personal sorrow did not make him falter in his work. Now, again, he was working with the Scripture, interpreting it, bettering his earlier translation, translating for the first time the books of Joshua through Chronicles.

Nor did he lack for either supporters or new disciples. It was at this time that John Rogers, the newly appointed chaplain to the English house at Antwerp, became his convert and friend.

Rogers came to Tyndale one day with news. His eyes were shining with excitement. "Now here is something to cheer your heart, my friend," he said, still puffing slightly from the steep climb to the little room.

Tyndale looked up from his work, one thin hand shading his eyes, and Rogers was suddenly struck with how fine-drawn the other man appeared. There was good reason for it, he admitted to himself, in the ascetic life that Tyndale led, the unremitting labor, the sorrow which had come upon him these past years.

"Good news?" Tyndale laid down his pen and straightened a little.

"The best," Rogers returned. "You remember how King Henry promised to have the Bible translated into English?"

Tyndale nodded. "That was several years ago. And only last year Convocation petitioned the king to fulfill his promise. But—"

Rogers held up an imperious hand. "Wait! Coverdale is going to put out a complete Bible—the first in English—and there is a chance the king *will allow it to circulate in England!*"

Tyndale sat perfectly still, almost stunned by the news. Then he said, "Then it will be printed in England, too? I thought Coverdale was here on the Continent."

"He is—he was—oh, I don't know where he is at the moment." The younger man was greatly stirred and stammered in reply. "But it will probably be printed in Germany."

Tyndale said, wonderingly, "And you think it will

be permitted in England?" as if he could not believe his ears.

"So they say. It is true this is only rumor, but I came straight to you as soon as I heard it, for I knew what this would mean to you."

Tyndale got up slowly, his face radiant. The thing he had worked for, prayed for, waited for all these years, might yet come to pass and the people of England would have their Bible at last.

9. BETRAYAL

(1535)

MANY CHANGES had taken place in England in the past few years. Since Wolsey's fall the king had gathered the reins firmly into his own hands, and churchmen had had to bow to his will. And after the divorce and his break with Rome, the king had become more tolerant of his subjects who were exiled abroad because of their beliefs.

Tyndale was easier in his mind these days. The hunted feeling that had been with him for so many years slackened, and he was happier than he had been for some time. He dined often with his merchant friends, and on Sundays he read to them from the Scripture, and it was said of his reading that it "proceeded so fruitfully, sweetly and gently from him . . . that it was a heavenly comfort and joy to the audience to hear him."

One evening at supper in a friend's house he met among the guests a young man lately come from England. He was tall and handsome, and when he was presented to Tyndale, his manner, which had been a bit swaggering, became humbly respectful.

He said, bowing low, "It is a great honor, Master Tyndale, to meet one who has so influenced the thought of our times, and whose great achievement has been to bring the Scriptures within the reach of the people."

This pleased Tyndale, for it showed an understanding of his motives, and he smiled at the young man. "Did you say your name was Phillips?" he asked, for he was not sure his ear had caught it correctly.

"Henry Phillips," the young man said, "and an admirer of yours and of that great martyr, John Frith."

Tyndale's smile faded. His grief for John still lay deep in his heart. "If he could have been spared," he murmured, "who knows what he might not have accomplished?"

"But may he not have accomplished even more," Phillips asked respectfully, "by his untimely death? None can forget him now. None can fail to revere him. I wish I had known him better."

Tyndale said quickly, "You knew him? You knew John?"

"Not well, alas. I took my degree at Oxford in civil law, and only met him once or twice. But who could fail to be impressed by even one meeting with so great a character?"

Tyndale sat down in the cushioned window embrasure and motioned Phillips to sit beside him. "So you were at Oxford when he was," he said gently. "Come, tell me about it."

The young man's smile was embarrassed, and he was quick to explain. "There is little to tell, Sir William. He was a canon and I was only a humble student." He leaned forward. "But you can tell *me* about him, for all the world knows that he was your great friend and disciple."

It was both pain and pleasure to speak of John. To make him come alive for this earnest young man who listened so attentively when he spoke. Before the evening was over, Phillips had so impressed Tyndale with his serious questions and deferential manner that the older man felt he might, in time, become another devoted friend and disciple.

And so he proved, coming frequently to the English house where Tyndale lived with Thomas Poyntz, to sit at Tyndale's feet with homage. They met, too, at the homes of various merchants. Phillips was apparently a man of leisure and seemed to be wealthy, for he had a servant with him. So close did they become, with Phillips ever in attendance, that he even lodged for a while in the same house.

Tyndale could not have been more surprised when Poyntz, his host, said to him one day, "Who is this Phillips I am forever stumbling over? He looks to be something of a rogue, I think."

"He is only a young man eager to learn the truth," Tyndale said in swift defense of his new acquaintance.

"You are intent on giving him instruction and see only the one side of him. But to me he rings as false as a counterfeit coin."

"I cannot understand why you feel that way." Tyndale was puzzled. He knew Poyntz was always thoughtful of his safety, but this was uncalled-for suspicion. "What have you against him?"

Poyntz could not answer. He muttered something about "not seeming true" and added, "I must go to Bergen-op-Zoom on business in a week or so, and I shall hope that young Phillips will have found other occupation before I return." Then, realizing how harsh this sounded and not wishing to hurt Tyndale, he added, "You must not be offended by what I say, Sir William. You know I am only thinking of you."

Tyndale nodded. He could have no more loyal friend than Thomas Poyntz. But he was troubled that his friend did not approve of Phillips. Surprisingly, it was only a day or so later that the young man told him he must go to Brussels for a while, and he and his servant disappeared from the city.

Soon thereafter Phillips' servant arrived at the English house to ask if Tyndale were at home. Poyntz, who was sitting in his doorway, told the man that the scholar was in, and he expected Phillips to come. But, strangely, Phillips did not appear.

It was only when Poyntz had left on his business trip that Phillips turned up. He came to Tyndale's room, looking so downcast that Tyndale said, "You must stay for dinner, Henry. You are looking unhappy. Did something happen to you in Brussels?"

Phillips sighed deeply. "Not in Brussels, but between Mechlin and here. I have lost my purse, and forty shillings in it."

"Now, that is something that is soon mended," Tyndale told him. Always generous with what he had, he took out his purse and counted some money into his visitor's hand. "There! I have given you forty shillings of my own, and now you can be yourself again."

Phillips brightened. "Now that I am rich once more," he said in sudden high spirits, "you shall dine with me! And I'll not take No for an answer."

But Tyndale said, "I cannot, for I am dining at a friend's house. You must come along." And he put on his cloak, for though it was late May there was still a chill in the air.

They went down the steep steps to the street floor and there, coming to the long, narrow entryway, the young man, with a great show of courtesy, insisted that Tyndale lead the way.

As they came out into the street, two men rose from benches placed on either side of the door. They caught hold of Tyndale's arms and told him harshly that he was under arrest. His first thought was of his friend, and he cast a quick backward glance, crying out, "Take cover!"

The men hustled him down the street and around the corner, but he no longer resisted. For Phillips still stood in the doorway, smiling, and his smile was evil.

10. TRIAL AND DEATH
(1535–1536)

ARREST WAS SOMETHING Tyndale had anticipated for many years; imprisonment and death were words he had long known might describe his own future. He was a man of great spiritual and moral strength, and he could face these things with more equanimity than most. But betrayal from one he had thought a friend was hard to bear.

In the months that followed, Tyndale's friends in the Merchant Adventurers worked desperately to save him. Poyntz was ruined by his devoted support of Tyndale, being finally imprisoned himself, and barely escaping with his life. Wife and children, the wealth and work of years, had to be abandoned when he fled to England for safety.

But nothing prevailed, for Henry Phillips had done his work well. The blackguard son of a prominent father, he had been forced to flee his native country when he had gambled away money his father had given him for another purpose. It was money that had caused his downfall in England, and it was for money that he had heartlessly betrayed Tyndale to the authorities in Brussels.

Deep in the dungeon cells of the massive castle of Vilvorde, the state prison of the Low Countries, William Tyndale spent the last months of his life. Although no word reached him, he knew that his friends were sparing no effort to save him. He knew that he had not been forgotten, for they had sent money to feed him, as was the custom.

But he knew, too, that the end had come. There would be a farce of a trial, in which he would once more be called upon to state his beliefs; there would be long hours of examination. But those arrayed against him had decided his guilt long years before. They would not let him escape.

The months dragged on. Tyndale was allowed no visitors who were friendly, but his simple dignity so impressed his keeper over the months that the man— and his daughter, as well—was converted to Tyndale's beliefs.

But even with a friendly keeper, the prison was dark and cold, and little liberty of any kind was permitted the prisoner. The chill of a Flemish winter must have been in the air when he wrote to the governor of the state prison. He said:

*I believe, right worshipful, that you are not un-
aware of what may have been determined concerning me. Wherefore I beg your lordship, and that by
the Lord Jesus, that if I am to remain here through
the winter, you will request the commissary to have
the kindness to send me, from the goods of mine
which he has, a warmer cap; for I suffer greatly from
cold in the head, and am afflicted by a perpetual
catarrh, which is increased in this cell; a warmer
coat also, for this which I have is very thin; a piece
of cloth to patch my leggings. My overcoat is worn
out; my shirts are also worn out. He has a woollen
shirt, if he will be good enough to send it. I have
also with him leggings of thicker cloth to put on
above; he has also warmer night caps. And I ask to
be allowed to have a lamp in the evening; it is indeed wearisome sitting alone in the dark. But most
of all I beg and beseech your clemency to be urgent
with the commissary, that he will kindly permit me
to have the Hebrew bible, Hebrew grammar, and
Hebrew dictionary, that I may pass the time in that
study. In return may you obtain what you most desire, so only that it be for the salvation of your soul.
But if any other decision has been taken concerning
me, to be carried out before winter, I will be patient,
abiding the will of God, to the glory of the grace of
my Lord Jesus Christ; whose Spirit, I pray, may ever
direct your heart. Amen.*

W. Tindalus

After the months of oral examination came even wearier months of written argument, for Tyndale had chosen to defend himself, and much of the trial was carried on by correspondence. But at last the farce was over. Condemned as a heretic, Tyndale was taken into the town of Vilvorde and there publicly degraded from the priesthood and handed over to the secular authorities for execution.

Early in October, 1536, in the public square of Vilvorde, William Tyndale, devoted servant of God, walked fearlessly to his death. Sentenced to be first strangled and then burned, his calm was unshaken as he was tied to the stake, and he lifted up his head and cried, in a loud and fervent voice, "Lord, open the king of England's eyes."

EPILOGUE

ONE YEAR LATER John Rogers, who had been Tyndale's disciple in Antwerp and who had helped him with the revision of the New Testament translation, was licensed by the king of England to put forth his Bible (known as Matthew's Bible) and two years after that, there being confusion in the land with two different Bibles available, Coverdale was asked to prepare another version. This was based on Matthew's Bible and Coverdale's former Bible and was issued as the Great Bible. This was "appointed to be read in Churches." Much of it was Tyndale's work.

Then, some years later, when the Roman Catholic Queen Mary was on the English throne, a group of reformers who had fled to Geneva for safety engaged in Bible translation and issued the Genevan Bible, the first one in which the text was divided into verses. This was the Bible cherished by the Puritans and our own Pilgrim Fathers. Still later, in Queen Elizabeth's time, the English bishops made their own translation, called the Bishops' Bible.

But it was not until 1582 that a Roman Catholic New Testament in the English language made its appearance. The Old Testament was not published until 1609–1610. The Rheims-Douai Bible, as this version was called, was a quite literal translation of the Latin Vulgate.

Finally, when still another ruler reigned over England—one who was genuinely interested in the Scriptures—there was a demand from many of the Puritans for a revision of the Bishops' Bible, which was still the "authorized" version, and King James I appointed more than fifty scholars to see to the work. Even with so many men to revise it, the work took four years; but in 1611 the King James Version, which is known to most students of the English Bible, was printed. Nine-tenths of the New Testament of this famous Bible was taken from Tyndale's translation, for his rich vocabulary, clear prose, and singing rhythms had had a lasting effect upon the language. He had left the English-speaking peoples a magnificent legacy.

Tyndale did not only die for his beliefs; he lived for them. The influence he exerted lived on for centuries after him, and, indeed, still lives today. There are not many men who have accomplished so much in so little time. There are not many men who have so truly dedicated their lives to others.

The tragedy of Tyndale was that he lived only a few

years too soon. Had he been born ten years later, his work would have been acclaimed by the very authorities who condemned it in his lifetime. He would not have had to live out his manhood in exile; he would have been an honored scholar in his own country.

The glory of Tyndale was that none of these things mattered to him. Only his work mattered, and to that he gave everything—his energies, his comfort, his very life. But his work has lived as the work of few others has lived, enshrined in the book to which men turn for solace and spiritual inspiration.